# Growing
# in the
# Image of God

# Growing in the Image of God

Carol Rausch Albright

Series editor: Ivan Timonin

© 2002 Novalis, Saint Paul University, Ottawa, Canada

Cover: Miriam Bloom
Layout: Caroline Gagnon

Business Office:
Novalis
49 Front Street East, 2nd Floor
Toronto, Ontario, Canada
M5E 1B3

Phone: 1-800-387-7164 or (416) 363-3303
Fax: 1-800-204-4140 or (416) 363-9409
E-mail: cservice@novalis.ca

National Library of Canada Cataloguing in Publication Data

Albright, Carol Rausch
Growing in the image of God / Carol Rausch Albright.

(Saint Paul University research series)
Includes bibliographical references and index.
ISBN 2-89507-269-8

1. Image of God. 2. Man (Christian theology) 3. Religion and science. I. Title. II.
Series.

BT702.A43 2002          233'.5          C2002-901967-2

Printed in Canada.

We acknowledge the financial support of the Government of Canada through
the Book Publishing Industry Development Program (BPIDP) for our publishing activities.

10 9 8 7 6 5 4 3 2 1    10 09 08 07 06 05 04 03 02

*To my husband, John R. Albright,*

*whose scientific knowledge reassures my understanding;*

*whose companionship makes the quest a grand adventure.*

# Contents

# Foreword

It's as if she had seen the Promised Land "from over Jordan"! Several years ago, a dear friend of Saint Paul University donated a substantial sum to be used to promote "the study and wider recognition of the relationship between faith (the reflection on and the 'practice' of faith) and science (the exact [or hard] sciences and human [or soft] sciences), especially in its cultural aspects."

After a lengthy debate, the Rector of Saint Paul University, Dr. Dale M. Schlitt, OMI, and the Vice Rector, Academic, Dr. Achiel Peelman, OMI, decided that the University would sponsor four public lectures in the field of science and religion in the year 2000 and later publish expanded versions of the lectures. They engaged me to write the letters, make the travel arrangements, and act as the University's interface with the authors.

In developing our concept, we wrote the following statement:

As the new millennium begins, and on a more sober note than much of the hyperbole surrounding that passage, Saint Paul University is proposing a series of four public lectures in the field of science and religion. The theme of these lectures, "Creation and Creature," will allow scope for our four principal speakers to explore both the scientific and the theological aspects of the theme, together with the nexus between them.

On the one hand, the question of creation itself may raise the relationship between chaos theory and an understanding of Genesis 1. On the question of creation's creatures, particularly humankind, there will be scope for exploration of "creatureliness," the *imago dei*, the Pauline proclamations [neither Jew nor Greek; neither male nor female], and the responsibility of humanity, as created, for the other creations of its Creator.

Four topics emerged in consultation with the four invited speakers: the possibility of a Christian theology of science; the question of creation out of chaos *vs.* creation *ex nihilo*; the evolution of human understanding of God; and "knowing God and nature in a postmodern world." In that order, the speakers were Dr. Donald Lococo, CSB, Assistant Professor of Christianity and Culture at the University of Saint Michael's College, Toronto; Rev. Dr. Sjoerd Bonting, formerly Professor of Biochemistry at the University of Nijmegen, Holland, and a priest of the Anglican Communion; Ms. Carol Albright, Midwest (United States) Regional Director of the Center for Theology and the Natural Sciences and former Executive Editor of *Zygon: Journal of Religion and Science*; and Dr. Jitse van der Meer, Professor of Biology at Redeemer College, Ancaster, Ontario, and founding director of the Pascal Centre for Advanced Studies in Faith and Science at Redeemer College.

The lectures took place in Spring and Autumn 2000. Regrettably, the woman whose gift made the series possible – and whose wish to remain anonymous we continue to honour – died just two weeks before the first lecture. But she was able to see, as if "from over Jordan," the land promised in return for her generosity by way of my letter to her, which set out for her the details about the proposed lecture series and plans for publication. Although many at Saint Paul University who knew her and valued her friendship miss her, the memory of her longstanding friendship and her devotion to the University will continue. These publications are the first installment on that memorial.

In the development and implementation of this project a number of people have participated by giving counsel and direction, by lending particular expertise at various stages. I would like to acknowledge my indebtedness, as series co-ordinator, to them all. The Rector, Dr. Dale M. Schlitt, OMI, and the then Vice Rector, Academic, Dr. Achiel Peelman, OMI, were the prime movers and directors of the project. Ms. Lucie Laplante, Executive Secretary to the Rector, provided administrative support and kept things on track. Professors Heather Eaton and James Pambrun of the Faculty of Theology, Saint Paul University, provided input and advice in the project's initial stages. Kevin Burns (Commissioning Editor), Anne Louise Mahoney (Managing Editor), Caroline Gagnon and Suzanne Latourelle (Designers, Novalis Graphic Design Studio), all of Novalis Publishing, advised and worked on the various stages of publicity for the lectures and on manuscript preparation and publication for the series. I would like to express my gratitude to all of them.

*Ivan Timonin*
*Series Editor*
*Spring 2002*

# Introduction

## The Conditions of Human Understanding

Our thoughts about ourselves, and our thoughts about God, inevitably rest within our sense of what our world is like and how it works. This is so even though some of us try hard to separate sacred and secular thought. Many of us believe that certain teachings about spiritual matters are eternally true. But even so, we cannot help but view these teachings through eyes conditioned by the intellectual and social milieu that moulds us – by prevailing understandings of "the way things really are."

A history of God-talk easily traces such correlations. For example, people who live with despotic authorities tend to believe in a fearsome God. In the Oriental Institute of Chicago, near my home, visitors encounter the glare of Babylonian stone deities, as rigid and intimidating as the laws of the rulers who sanctioned their creation. On the other hand, the idea of God as the giver of the book of life, with its continuity of understandings, may draw on the innovation of scrolls – books – which were seen as a wondrous way of retaining and transmitting culture through means more permanent than human memory. The metaphor of a God who created a world as wonderful as clockwork traces back to Nicole Oresme in medieval Paris,[1] where the clock escapement mechanism was hailed as a marvellous advance and great clocks were a matter of civic pride. In the seventeenth century, Sir Isaac Newton's wonderfully logical laws of motion reinforced the notion of a God of logic: a God who set the world in motion like clockwork. Beginning in the nineteenth century, theology struggled with ideas of the evolutionary origin of present life forms, and views of religious belief related to psychoanalytic thinking; these developments have affected our religious beliefs and doubts. Today, human perceptions of the Deity continue to change, even within the Judeo-Christian tradition. The fact is, we can only understand our universe, and our place within it, using the tools we have: our brain, our observations and what we are taught by others.

Although we can study the lessons of the past, the metaphors and metaphysical assumptions of our own age shape our views on a deep level. We use them as reference points to comprehend what is beyond our comprehension. The same limitations apply to scientific knowledge. As Michael Polanyi made clear in his celebrated book *Personal Knowledge,* "all claims to objective knowledge are at the same time personal to the speaker or writer, because they are grounded in…a set of personal convictions about the nature of reality…which cannot itself be personally verified."[2] Science operates on the *belief* that reality is consistent and can be explored through the scientific method.

Because we necessarily understand with a human brain, we "humanize" everything we think about – that is, we think of it through our human experience and reasoning. That is the limitation – and the glory – of being human. Yet, we should not sell this ability short.

This brain of ours has enabled our species to survive and thrive. It has evolved over the millennia in tandem with the world where we live, and it has proven highly useful (if not always virtuous). Because it enables our species to get along in the world, it must indicate *something* about what the world is really like. Even though it has limitations, it provides us with information correlated with the "really real." Thus, the nature of our brain and the messages it generates must provide some clues to the nature of the world itself. However, as we have already seen, we are creatures of our time and place as well as of our neurophysiology.

Because we are necessarily limited, we are not required to understand all truth for all time. We are responsible for understanding what we can in our own time, and for doing what needs to be done at the time. Our limitations may be frustrating, but we must live with them. Long before our time, the Greeks and the

Hebrews were aware of the risks of hubris, of a claim to knowledge that is beyond our scope. The eighteenth-century German philosopher Immanuel Kant reinforced their cautionary analysis in his *Critique of Pure Reason,* in which he analyzed the limits of rationality as a means to truth.[3]

Scientists today may be seen as heirs of Kant, because they are well aware of the limits of human knowledge. They regard scientific findings as always in need of confirmation, forever subject to challenge, modification and even overthrow. As Miguel de Unamuno observed, "True science teaches, above all, to doubt and be ignorant."[4] This very caution is a basic reason why science has in the last few centuries learned so much about our universe. But even scientific research is influenced by the prevailing opinions of the times. As Mariano Artigas observes, "experiments are planned and interpreted using concepts that cannot be reduced to mere observation. Nothing like 'pure empirical data' exists, and so experimental testing does not consist in merely comparing theories and empirical data."[5] Today it is generally acknowledged that all kinds of data and experiments are "theory laden," and that theories cannot be proven using only the results of observation. Along these lines, philosophers speak about the "underdetermination" of theories by empirical facts as a real feature of the scientific procedure.[6]

# Chapter 1

# Complexity Theory and Holism Challenge Our Assumptions

As persons of the early twenty-first century, we may ask these questions: What emerging understandings are entering our intellectual milieu and the larger culture today? How are such new understandings shaping our images of human beings and, if we are theists, our understandings of the Originator and Sustainer of our universe? Finally, how can these understandings shed light on how best to live our lives, now, in the era we inhabit and help to shape?

Of course, there are many emerging insights in our era – so many that to build an analysis upon only a few seems foolish. We may approach this problem by seeking to identify trends of thought that comprise or influence many subdisciplines. For cultures do tend to change holistically. Various developments interact and move in tandem.

This essay aims to trace two such overarching trends, which in turn are linked with one another. We will explore where they may be taking our thinking about ourselves and our responsibilities, and will also ask whether, and how, such insights might influence our understanding of the Image of God.

We are dealing here with paradigm shifts, which tend to build up gradually, then finally take place quickly. Thomas Kuhn has traced the process within science in his classic *The Structure of Scientific Revolutions*.[7] A shift begins as increasing numbers of research results do not fit comfortably within the reigning paradigm, and doubts and new theories begin to arise. Established scholars may see these aberrant findings as threats to their intellectual commitments and their career investments. They may find ways to undermine the new thinking and punish its advocates. At some point, however, the balance of evidence becomes such that the new theories become the new paradigm. Typically, the old paradigm then becomes the object of more derision than it actually deserves. Even today, centuries after most people learned that the earth is round, "flat-earther" remains an insult. Two centuries have elapsed since French naturalist Jean-Baptiste de Monet de Lamarck worked out his theories of evolution by inheritance of acquired characteristics, and 150 years since he was shown to be wrong about inheritance.[8] But "Lamarckian" is still a term of derision in biological circles, even though Lamarck actually made major contributions to understandings of the evolutionary process.

Nonetheless, assumptions based on the outgoing paradigm tend to survive in the popular culture long after science has moved on. They often support the conventional wisdom. For example, Niels Bohr's model of the atom as a miniature solar system, propounded almost a century ago and long since discarded by particle physics, remains the popular image of the structure of an atom. And while quantum physics (first proposed in the early 1920s) forms the basis of the Internet and the entire communications revolution, it has barely begun to penetrate the popular intellectual tool kit in discussions of "uncertainty."

Of course, shifts in understanding also occur within arenas other than science. One example is the transition from government by a powerful monarchy to various forms of democracy in the West. Here, as in other major cultural or intellectual changes, the process was not uniform in time or geography and did not follow precisely the same pattern in all places. However, writ large, parallel cultural changes did occur over large areas within the same historic periods, influenced not only by creative leadership, but also by changes in technology and communication – for example, the telegraph, steam transportation, and periodical publishing – and by such social inventions as the permanent government bureaucracy and the corporation. Paradigm shifts, whether in science, in governance, or in other arenas, inevitably influence our thinking about God's action and human responsibility.

Here we will examine two scientific paradigm shifts of our own day – one well established, the other still in formation. Both have had a ripple effect on other understandings, and we may anticipate that their influence will continue to expand.

The first trend concerns scientific understandings of *self-organization* and *emergence*. By self-organization we mean observations that natural systems have a tendency to become more intricately organized all by themselves, without human intervention. New and unforeseen phenomena occur as a result; this process is called *emergence*. Self-organization and emergence have been discerned, by various observers, in systems ranging from the subatomic to the economic and the cosmic. These conclusions are relatively new, and not all scholars agree about them. However, scholars in a variety of disciplines refer to them, with increasing frequency, as a more or less settled assumption. As a group, these studies are known as *complexity studies*. They will probably have a growing influence on how we think about "the way things really are."

The second trend poses a challenge to long-standing dualistic thinking. This trend concerns the understanding that energy and matter not only interact but are actually interchangeable, as Albert Einstein famously suggested in his 1905 publication of the Special Theory of Relativity and its central formula, $E = mc^2$. As relativistic thinking develops, it raises problems for distinctions between matter and energy, and similarly, between substance and process and between matter and mind. Although dualistic assumptions are persistent and widespread, the physics of our day demands their reformulation.

In the sections that follow, I will discuss in more detail the implications of the two paradigm shifts that I have sketched, and ways in which they interact. For example, both the development and functioning of the human brain and development of the mind and personality may be seen as more dynamic and less fixed than previous thinking had admitted. Spiritual development is a related consideration.

Finally, we take a major step, from a focus on the human personality to a discussion of the effects that the new paradigms may have on our understanding of the Image of God, and even of the Deity per se. I will suggest that, as personalities gain complexity, they may also increase in spiritual development and better reflect the Image of God.

## 1.1 The Impact of Complexity Theory

How the world as we know it came to be so well organized presents something of a puzzle. By contrast, strong theories about the development of disorder and disorganization have been around for 150 years. In order to understand the newer theories about self-organization, we need to discuss theories of *dis*organization, otherwise known as studies of *entropy*.

## Entropy

The Second Law of Thermodynamics was first proposed by the German physicist Rudolf Clausius in 1850.[9] Today it stands as one of the foundational laws of science. In brief, it states that in a closed system, there will be an inevitable increase in entropy. Let us define these terms.

A *closed system* simply means a system which no matter or energy can enter or leave. A closed system is completely self-contained. Obviously, our earth is not a closed system, since we daily receive energy from the sun, and we radiate energy to space. The city of Chicago, where I live, is not a closed system, since gasoline and electricity and other sources of energy come into town every day. So do groceries and hardware items and new clothes. And every day, Chicago exports TV broadcasts and financial services and railway locomotives. It also exports emissions and hauls trash to the dump. You and I are not closed systems. Every day we "import" food and water and air. We use energy in our daily rounds, and we exhale carbon dioxide, radiate heat, and excrete bodily wastes. Unlike you or me or Chicago, the universe as a whole is by definition a closed system, since nothing can enter or leave it. The Second Law of Thermodynamics applies most broadly to the entire universe.

Now, what is entropy? We can look at it in terms of organization: the more entropy increases, the less things are organized. In other words, the Second Law of Thermodynamics indicates that everything naturally runs to disorder. Anyone who has ever taken care of a home can identify with this! Now suppose that things get really out of hand, and as time goes by, all the papers become spread quite evenly around the house, as do all the dirty dishes, and all the dustballs, until finally, every space looks exactly like every other space. And then everything in the house turns to dustballs! As applied to the entire universe, the Second Law predicts that finally, at the end of time, all matter will be evenly distributed, everything will be the same temperature, and there will be no differentiation at all. Everything that exists will have become a sort of cosmic mush.

Living systems – which, remember, are not closed systems – can counteract entropy for a time, just as you and I do when we file the papers and put the dishes back in the cupboard and sweep up the dustballs. Living things can use food and oxygen to build organized tissues and to repair injuries. Living things have the energy to do this because they import energy, in the form of food, and export disorder, in the form of bodily wastes. But eventually, says the Second Law, entropy will catch up with us all. Not only will our individual lives end in death, but all life will cease.

Why will the universe "run down"? At the time of the Big Bang, an enormous amount of energy was released. For reasons that are not well understood, it became distributed unevenly, so there was lots of potential energy in the opportunity to redistribute it. But by the end of time, the energy will have been spread evenly around the universe, and there will be no possibility to accomplish any more work, since work by definition involves the redistribution of energy. So the theory goes. When you think about it, this is a rather gloomy theory. In spite of all our best efforts, it says, all will eventually come to nothing. Perhaps the poet T.S. Eliot was influenced by this type of thinking when he wrote his poem "The Hollow Men" in 1925. It concludes:

> This is the way the world ends
> This is the way the world ends
> This is the way the world ends
> Not with a bang, but a whimper.

## Complexity

Self-organization appears to counteract the disintegrative forces of entropy. However, theories of self-organization nest within the larger framework already described. I have neither the information nor the standing to challenge the Second Law of Thermodynamics. But theories about self-organization do run in quite a different direction, and their mood seems more hopeful. Such theories are converging from various disciplines. The work is centred at a "think tank" in New Mexico called the Santa Fe Institute. Scholars are attracted there because they believe they have discerned, in their differing disciplines, processes of complexification. Key figures at Santa Fe have included Nobel Prize-winning physicists Murray Gell-Mann and Philip Anderson, biologist Stuart Kauffman, artificial intelligence specialist John Holland, and Nobelist-economist Kenneth Arrow.

A single definition of complexity is difficult to find, even in books by the Santa Fe crowd. Some, such as Gell-Mann, correlate complexity with the length of the computer code necessary to describe an entity: the more nonrepetitive bits of information are required, the more complex is the entity. (A long computer code does not indicate complexity if it contains sequences that repeat over and over as, for example, when describing fractals.)[10] This is a telling definition, but not everyone is comfortable thinking about the implications of information in computer codes. So for our purposes, let us use the term "complexity" to denote the presence of a web of interlinked and active connections: the more intricate the web, the more complex the entity. Complexification is a process that increases complexity. And, to clarify the definition, complexity as used here does not mean merely complicated. Consider a life that pulls us in many directions at once, where our efforts do not reinforce one another but may in fact cancel each other out. Such a life is complicated; it is not complex. A life that is complex is integrated. It may include many aspects, but these tend to reinforce one another and to work in synergy.

Complexification can occur when we ourselves bring about link-ups in patterns so that they become increasingly meaningful and productive. A familiar example might be the creation of a network of colleagues who interact meaningfully among themselves, with the result that things get accomplished that none could do alone. In fact, a complex network of persons might reach a level of interaction and achievement that would not have been predicted by an outside observer, and something new may emerge. But a complicated group might grind to a halt and accomplish very little. A premier example of a complex group might be the founders of the New Physics in the 1920s and 1930s. Many had been friends since secondary school, and they interacted primarily in Budapest, Copenhagen, Göttingen, and Cambridge, England.

Another example might be the group of men who bravely founded a form of democratic government that had never been seen before, and founded it so well that it has lasted more than two centuries – more than any other republic in history except the relatively isolated Swiss confederation. Whatever the United States has become in the intervening years, it seems clear in retrospect that its founders were in fact a complex group who created something new under the sun.

It is surprising to note that in nature – even nonliving nature – things often become more and more complex all by themselves. They become linked into increasingly complex entities. These entities are known as self-organizing systems. They exist almost everywhere. In fact, entities in nature, left to their own devices, will join together. Atoms form molecules, which form compounds, which recombine to form more complex compounds, until they stand on the threshold of life. Viruses may or may not be defined as alive; they must infiltrate living cells in order to replicate (and often cause disease in the process). Living organisms may be one-celled or more complex. Not everything that exists will complexify; much will remain simple. There are still many more bacteria than mammals. But over eons of time, increasingly complex and intelligent forms of life have appeared. Furthermore, complexification occurs not only among relatively simple entities but also in sentient life forms. And social networks, and even economic systems tend to complexify. They draw in more resources and players in patterns of increasingly complex interaction.

### Emergence

One of the important hallmarks of complexification is that it gives rise to phenomena that are new and that could not be predicted by observing their predecessors. These new entities are called emergent phenomena. Water is a simple example: it is very different from its "parents," hydrogen and oxygen. If the results of emergence are "successful," the new substance will probably complexify again and produce more emergents. Water becomes involved in more complex chemical bonds, forming highly complex compounds, including some of the building blocks of cells.

And from these building blocks, cells may form. Physicist Paul Davies, a Templeton Prize winner, has described the phenomenon as follows:

> The universe is undeniably complex, but its complexity is of an organized variety. Moreover, this organization was not built into the universe at its origin. It has emerged from primeval chaos in a sequence of self-organizing processes that have progressively enriched and complexified the evolving universe in a more or less unidirectional manner.[11]

Physicists have seen this process with elementary particles – for example, the construction of atomic nuclei out of protons and neutrons in a way that exemplifies collective internal motion. The nuclei have a structure that emerges from the interaction of their components.

In the biological sciences, parallel observations have been made. Lynn Margulis, for example, helped to bring about a paradigm shift through years of advocating a theory when there initially was little support for it. She maintained that "parasitism and symbiosis were the driving forces in the evolution of cellular complexity."[12] There are two basic kinds of cells – prokaryotes, or bacteria, and eukaryotes, cells with nuclei. Margulis collected the evidence to support her view that the main internal structures of eukaryotic cells did not originate within the cells but are descended from independent living creatures that invaded the cells from outside like carriers of an infectious disease.[13] Thus, a single-celled entity has complexified by taking in smaller organelles. However, a different complexification strategy is seen in the case of slime moulds. These single-celled organisms may form colonies that collaborate in ingestion and excretion. The moulds that collaborate tend to fare better than those that go it alone.[14]

Economists see complexification in the evolution of economic systems. Even during the first millennium BCE, economies that were geographically and politically able to combine resources from several surrounding cultures far surpassed economies that were isolated. Egypt and Rome are examples. The process has continued, as exchange of technological and social inventions has enabled peoples and technologies to work together in ever more complex ways, and new kinds of social organization have emerged. Today the world faces a critical time of decision regarding the globalization of technology, communications and international capital; the choices of the next two decades may well decide how the world spends the next two centuries.

Thus, from molecules to multinational organizations, the tendency to complexify may be observed, and the emergent "inventions" – biological, technical or social – often survive and thrive. However, the process also has a Darwinian character. Every emergent entity encounters challenges from its environment. Those that are able to adapt to changing and challenging conditions are most likely to survive. For example, bacteria are poisoned by substances that fungi produce to defend themselves against germs. Human beings (who are eukaryotes) use these substances to combat bacteria (prokaryotes) and call them antibiotics. Bacteria in turn have adapted and become resistant to antibiotics. In another example, grazing animals may encounter a drought, but they may survive if they move on to greener pastures. Economic systems that allow for experiment while also providing some reliable conditions seem to do better than those with rigidly prescribed five-year plans – or those with a chaotic lack of any rules. Successful systems are always adapting, and they have both the freedom and the reliable resources that allow them to adapt. That is why these systems have come to be called complex adaptive systems.

## Order and disorder

As we have just seen in regard to economic systems, complexity develops best where there is not only freedom but order. Complex adaptive systems at all levels are found most robustly on the cusp between order and openness. Under these advantageous circumstances, some conditions are predictable; they can be depended upon. However, there is also room for experiment and choice, trial and error. Complexifying systems are not found at an extreme of either order or disorder. A crystal is a very orderly phenomenon, but it is very static. At the other extreme we have the example in which "everything in the house has turned to dustballs." There is no orderly design whatsoever. Everything has the same density and the same temperature. Because energy is evenly distributed, there can be no transfer of energy and hence no work can be accomplished: no life, no dynamism here. Life and dynamism, in other words, thrive where there is some order and some disorder. In order for complexification and emergence to occur, there needs to be some lawfulness and some openness, some predictability and some contingency. There needs to be some dependability and some freedom.

This emphasis upon trial and error, upon contingency and chance, and upon interactions along multiple vectors, is at odds with viewing order as good and chaos as bad. It also denies the final validity of linear thinking in which developments must follow a logical progression. This new vision of "the way things really are" expects unpredictable emergent events and entities, networks, feedback loops and dynamic developments.

### Human complexity

What does all this theoretical discussion have to do with us human beings? Have processes of complexification had any effect on how we came to be? Has complexity theory anything to say about who we are, how we should be, and the trajectory of our lives?

In fact, our human bodies, like the bodies of all mammals, are extremely complex adaptive systems. For example, they maintain homeostasis – a balance of the hormones and gases and sugars and body temperature necessary to a healthy body – by continually adapting. They are never quite at rest. Take a deep breath – and hold it! That is not breathing, and it won't keep you alive for very long. Breathe out carbon dioxide, breathe in oxygen – adapt, adapt, adapt.

The body has a number of systems that keep it alive. These include the digestive system, the respiratory system, the circulatory, endocrine, nervous and musculoskeletal systems. Each system has many complex information feedback loops within itself so that, for example, the respiratory system automatically maintains breathing. But the respiratory system has links to the circulatory system, as it acts to maintain the proper balance of blood gases; these, in turn, are affected by musculoskeletal activity, and so it goes. Some of the adaptive activities take place with no need for input from the brain – for example, the kidneys "know" when the blood contains too much or too little calcium, and excrete calcium accordingly (calcium levels are also affected by the parathyroid glands through another feedback loop). Yet, the brain itself affects – and is affected by – conditions throughout the body.

## Complexity and the brain

The brain is the body's most complex system of all. In fact, for its size, the organ that we each carry around within our skull is the most complex natural system in the entire universe, so far as we know. To date, the long process of complexification in the evolution of the universe seems to have peaked right here. (It may not be the end of the story, though, because the universe presumably has a long way yet to run.) There are something like one hundred thousand million neurons in the brain – a number that rivals the number of stars in our galaxy. The number of connections among them is about one thousand million million, and the total length of this "wiring" is roughly one hundred thousand kilometres.[15] How are all these units organized? In his new book, *A Mind So Rare*, Merlin Donald provides a brief description. The cortex, or outer layer of the human brain, is organized into about six hundred thousand columnar units, each roughly half a millimetre in diameter. Each column contains about one hundred thousand neurons,

> woven into various brain-wide networks by millions of long communication fibers. These networks can respond to complex intellectual and emotional challenges with amazing speed and unity. The sheer number and complexity of these agglomerations, all contained inside a single human brain, exceed those of the entire global electronic highway, by many orders of magnitude....

> But this surely underestimates the real power of such a network. Neurons are far more flexible and have many more ways of communicating, both electrical and chemical, than the components of any known computer....

On a local scale, each column is a self-contained network in itself, with a fixed internal wiring diagram, or architecture. But it has no fixed pattern of connectivity to start. That distinction is important because while the basic columnar architecture is innate, its connectivity pattern is set by experience. Each of these columnar devices has countless interconnection points, or synapses, which connect neurons to one another in various patterns. This allows them to be wired up in various ways as the brain grows and develops and introduces a degree of flexibility or plasticity in their development.[16]

In order to link up with other neurons, each neuron can sprout long, hairlike extensions called axons. To catch incoming signals, neurons have bushy structures called dendrites. An axon from one neuron links up with a dendrite from another at a junction called a synapse. As we have seen, neurons may be organized in assemblies and subassemblies, so that one signal may be passed on to multiple other neurons; in fact, one neuron can be linked with as many as ten thousand others.[17] Information is transmitted through the release and absorption of chemical neurotransmitters, whose names, like serotonin and norepinephrine, are becoming somewhat familiar to us as they are affected by medications such as Prozac.

This complex organ inside our skulls can be a difficult thing to keep on course. It can so easily fall off the cusp of complexification into too much order and lack of flexible response, on the one hand, or, on the other hand, into too much disorder and chaos. This is both a blessing and a vulnerability.

### The self-organizing brain

It may appear that we are careering around in a rather dangerous machine, like a Lamborghini on a mountain road. The brain can take us many places, and our job seems to be to steer and control it – "mind over matter." Or, perhaps, the need may be to find the right combination of psychoactive drugs to keep the machine on course. In fact, though, the problem is not all that simple.

A normal brain, of course, produces a wide variety of thoughts, on matters from buying mutual funds to recalling the name of a friend to deciding what to prepare for dinner. It also generates emotional responses to the rise or fall of the mutual fund, the behaviour of the friend, or the prospect of a good meal. It may remember times shared with that friend ten years ago and try to project the mutual fund's behaviour ten years into the future. In addition, our brain has very basic responses regarding territory and survival, rituals and sexual attraction. Quite a vehicle, that brain of ours!

There is a lot of variation among brains. Not only do they function differently from one another, they even look different. Even in gross appearance, they are as various as faces are. The location of functions within brains are not always the same from one person to another. For a long time, it was believed that all the differences among our individual brains, our intelligence, and our talents were a fixed endowment, inherited through our genes. Perhaps God was the ultimate designer, but the genes were the proximate cause. However, it turns out that the process is not so straightforward. The brain has many millions of neurons, but it has recently been shown that the human genome has only about thirty thousand genes. The design of the brain is simply too complex for the genome to specify. The genome does not provide that much information. Thus, we are not simply at the mercy of the genetic brain lottery. We actually help to design our brain as we go along. And the circumstances we live in – our family, our culture, even our nutrition – are co-designers with us. So, not even identical twins – not even a cloned pair – will turn out to be identical individuals.

The first few years of life have a profound influence on the architecture of a person's brain. In the brains of infants and toddlers there is a process called programmed cell death. The infant brain comes equipped with an overabundance of neurons. Those that are put to use will continue to live and thrive with activity. Those that are not used are programmed to self-destruct. There is actually more neuron death in the brains of small children than occurs in normal aging. The neuronal selection process in children has a significant influence on their brain structure. This provides a physical reason why early childhood experience has such an important effect on personality and intelligence.

However, we are not completely locked into the consequences of our early years. The brain's interconnections do remain plastic – physically responsive to experience – throughout life, although the ability is less pronounced in adults than in children.[18] Brain networks are strengthened with use, and neurons can sprout new connections among themselves as needed. Conversely, neurons and neural networks that are not stimulated tend to lose vigour.

For many years it was believed that no new neurons could be formed in the brain of an adult human, but we may be in the midst of a paradigm shift on that very issue. Recent findings indicate that there is neurogenesis in the brains of adult humans, and that this takes place even in areas involved in learning and memory. While some neuroscientists have reported neurogenesis in the neocortex, others dispute this claim.[19] In any case, new neurons do apparently grow in adult brains at the rate of thousands per day. And new cells seem to develop in greater abundance and survive longer in people who are mentally and physically active. So, even in the brains of adult human beings, the watchword is "use it or lose it."[20]

Thus, experience plays a role in the structure of our brain: in its capacity, its connections, its habitual ways of operating. And it is important to keep in mind that the influential experiences may be inner or outer, self-generated or interactive. That is, they may involve inner thoughts, decisions and feelings and/or interactions with other people, with the natural world, or even with the virtual world.[21]

These inner and outer experiences are not entirely beyond our control. We are not simply pawns of fate. Certainly, randomness and "luck" do play a role in the course of our lives. But our own thoughts, decisions, and responses to experience also seem to play a crucial part in how our brains develop physically. Our choices not only affect what happens, but they also affect who we actually become, not only mentally, but even physiologically. Clearly, these findings indicate that we are more than a "pack of neurons," as Francis Crick famously dubbed the human persona.[22]

Roger Sperry,[23] winner of the Nobel Prize for his work on the difference between left brain and right brain, physicist George Ellis[24] and others concur that the brain's activity is not simply the product of the neurons we happen to have, acting in response to the experiences we encounter. Neurons do this work, but in a highly complex way.

We could call the brain's process a combination of "bottom-up" and "top-down." "Bottom-up" points to the activities of neurons per se. "Top-down" indicates the action of our embodied goals and values, for these do in fact have their physiological correlates within the brain's structure. They may be mobilized consciously; they also form part of the panoply of neuronal activities brought to bear on a situation. The values and choices of a lifetime form a strong organizing matrix for psychological activity, and their use is vital in the formation of human character. Although pioneering psychologist William James did not have all these neuroscientific findings available to him, he understood the process intuitively. At the turn of the last century, he wrote:

> The normal evolution of character chiefly consist[s] in the straightening out and unifying of the inner self. [Parts of the personality begin as] a comparative chaos within us – they must end by forming a stable system of functions in right subordination. Unhappiness is apt to characterize the period of order-making and struggle.[25]

James acknowledges that

> [t]he process of remedying inner incompleteness and reducing inner discord is a general psychological process which may take place with any sort of mental material and need not necessarily assume the religious form…. [Inner unity and peace] may come gradually or…occur abruptly…through altered feelings or through altered powers of action;…through new intellectual insights, or through experiences which we shall…have to designate as "mystical." However it comes, it brings a characteristic sort of relief; and never with such extreme relief as when it is cast into the religious mould…[bringing] a firmness, sta-

bility, and equilibrium succeeding a period of storm and stress and inconsistency.[26]

James saw that the experiences, choices and values of a lifetime mould the structure of character. Today, we can conclude as well that the structures of the neural connections almost certainly are modified in the process. These modifications, then, contribute to the further complexification of character.

### Embodiment of mind

Complexification in fact involves the whole person, and not only the brain. In fact, every part of a person's body may become involved in such processes, because the brain and the rest of the body are continually interactive. Thus, values and commitments affect not only brain activities, but other embodied processes as well. As a dramatic example, suppose you are about to undergo major surgery. You believe God loves you and God's spirit will guide the surgeon's hand. You know the chaplain is sitting with your spouse, and that folks from your church will bring a casserole dinner for your family. You are calmer and steadier than the patient next in line who shares none of these experiences. And, other things being equal, your outcome is likely to be better.

Recent research supports this claim. I will cite only a few of many studies pointing in this direction. (1) Heart surgery patients who are religious have 20 per cent shorter post-operative hospital stays than nonreligious patients.[27] (2) In a study of 1,718 older adults done over six years, immune function was better among frequent church attenders than among infrequent attenders.[28] (3) In a sixteen-year mortality study of 3,900 carefully matched subjects in eleven religious and eleven nonreligious kibbutzim in Israel, 69 persons in religious settings died, compared with 199 in secular settings.[29] (4) A prospective cohort study of 1,931 older residents of Marin County, California, found that those who attended religious services even occasionally were 24 per cent less likely to die than nonattenders during the five-year follow-up, even after controlling for age, sex, marital status, number of chronic diseases, lower-body disability, balance problems, exercise, smoking, alcohol use, weight, social functioning, social support and depression.[30]

Apparently, though, all religious beliefs are not equally helpful. In a study of 577 hospitalized medically ill patients age 55 or older, for example, beliefs in a punitive God and demonic forces were associated with worse mental and physical health, while beliefs in a benevolent God, collaboration with God, and giving religious help to others were associated with more positive outcomes.[31]

## 1.2 The Rise of Holistic Thinking

Now let us turn to the second shift in scientific thinking that we are considering: the rise of holistic thinking and its challenge to dualisms. This development, like complexity theory, inevitably interacts with established ideas about who we are as human beings and how we fit into the larger scheme of things. Complexity theory itself raises a challenge to dualisms and, as noted above, the revolution in thought posed by the New Physics also underlines the need for reformulation of old dualisms.

### A quick look at dualisms

The history of dualisms in religious and philosophical thought is so long and complicated that we cannot adequately summarize it here. But some effort in this direction is necessary in order that we may be clear about the terms we will use in our further discussion. The following observations lift up some of the relevant issues.

Dualism in Judeo-Christian thought has roots in a Persian religion, Zoroastrianism. As early as the seventh century BCE, Persians had adopted a religion whose prophet was Zoroaster, a.k.a. Zarathustra. According to this world view, the principle of goodness and light, known as Ahura Mazda or Ormazd, stands opposed to the principle of evil and darkness, known as Ahriman. The cosmic struggle between these two principles is seen as the central drama of world history. [32]

This dualistic view entered Judaism in the sixth century BCE, when the Persians liberated the children of Israel from their Babylonian captivity. The Israelites adopted the dualism of their liberators; before the captivity, these views were not prevalent in Hebrew religious thinking, judging by their written records. Needless to say, such dualistic beliefs remain commonplace in Judeo-Christian religious thought even to the present day.

The Greeks bequeathed to us a more cerebral form of dualism that focused on philosophy and had consequences for ethics. In the fourth century BCE, Plato divided reality into "form" and "matter." Forms were "the original, eternal transcendent archetypes of things, existing prior to things and apart from them, and thus uninfluenced by the changes to which they are subject."[33] Not simply abstractions, the forms were seen as having the character of substantiality. Matter was "formless, space-filling mass" having a lower order of existence; it was elevated insofar as it took on form.[34] Virtue or goodness resided in forms, not in matter.

Because the New Testament was written during a time when Greek thought was prevalent, the New Testament writers, who were Jews at heart, adapted Greek categories of form and matter to express their new and vibrant insights, as illustrated by Saint Paul's advice to the Galatians: "Live by the Spirit, I say, and do not gratify the desires of the flesh," he advised, for "what the flesh desires is opposed to the Spirit, and what the Spirit desires is opposed to the flesh; for these are opposed to each other, to prevent you from doing what you want" (Galatians 5:16-17, NRSV). Parallels may be observed between Paul's "Spirit" and the Greek concept of "form" and between Paul's concept of "flesh" and the Greek concept of "matter." Efforts to mortify the body – through ascetic and even self-punitive behaviour – have aimed to maximize virtue; such efforts have existed within many traditions.

As we have seen, "forms" were thought to have "substance." What is "substance"? "By substance we can mean nothing else than a thing which so exists that it needs no other thing in order to exist."[35] It is not difficult to see how the category "substance" came to denote the very nature of God. Thus there was a connection between thoughts about "form" and concepts of God.

Through the centuries, efforts were made to reconcile dualisms and also to reformulate dualistic thinking.

The idea of substance as the ultimate category was continued in the great work of Saint Thomas Aquinas. "That which requires nothing other than itself in order to exist" he called "substance" – the category of God. The Deity was expressed through relationships – within the Divine Life itself (i.e., the Trinity) and also externally, so that "the internally generative God is the externally creative God who brings forth a world." However, "substance" was seen as the primary category, and action as secondary.[36]

Such assumptions informed the early eras of scientific investigation, but dualistic distinctions also evolved over time. The original concern with form and matter, and with the substance of God and the action that underlies matter, carried over into an underlying assumption that things are somehow more "real" than processes. But things became identified with mass, and processes with energy. During the seventeenth century, one of the greatest scientific geniuses of all time, Sir Isaac Newton, who clearly accepted the theory of the Unmoved Mover, distinguished between mass and energy, although he did not use those terms. Yet, he also found a way to combine mass and energy in a single concept. One of his great contributions was to specify the *quantity* of motion. This quantity, which today we call *momentum,* is the mathematical product of the *velocity* at which something moves and the *mass* of what moves.

In the early seventeenth century, however, René Descartes proposed that the nature of both space and objects in the world is primarily process, whereas God is substance. He accomplished this by defining space and objects in terms of their *extension,* which he basically saw in terms of *motion.* Although Descartes is known for his mind/body dualism, he distinguished both mind and body from God: both, he said, depend upon God for existence, since God is basically substance. In Descartes' view, God, the Unmoved Mover, had given the world a certain fixed quantity of *motion,* which in Descartes' definition was a combination of mass and energy much like Newton's momentum.[37] (This assertion was a precursor to the later theory of the conservation of energy.)

By the late seventeenth century, Gottfried Wilhelm Leibniz had seen into the idea of momentum well enough to conceptualize *energy,* although he did not use that term. He distinguished between mass and energy, but through his concept of potential energy he furthered the understanding of how the two may be combined.

Only with the advent of Albert Einstein's Special Theory of Relativity (1905) did it begin to become clear that, ultimately, matter and energy are identical. Matter can be transformed into energy, and energy into matter. Rather than referring to conservation of energy per se, we should speak in terms of conservation of matter/energy. Quantum mechanics furthered this development by showing that matter/energy could sometimes be understood as a particle (or thing) and sometimes as a wave (or process). Whatever exists, fundamentally, can be manifested as either matter or energy. For at a very basic level, no real distinction exists between the two – only between what is, and what is not. The basic question – a question once answered with the concept of the Unmoved Mover – remains: Why is there something rather than nothing?

In our everyday lives, of course, we continue to operate with our ordinary dualistic thinking in the physical realm. We think in terms of things, on the one hand, and processes, on the other. Our language expresses this by its use of nouns to refer to things and verbs to refer to processes. We make some exceptions. Educated people know that matter is transformed into energy in the interior of the sun. There, hydrogen loses mass on becoming helium, and the "missing" mass is transformed into energy: life-giving warmth and light. Matter is also turned into energy in the generation of atomic power from enriched uranium. But by and large, we believe we can still tell the difference between energy and matter, or between process and substance, or between mind and brain.

## Mind/brain and holism

Now we can begin to see the point of this brief historical digression. For today, such dualistic boundaries seem increasingly blurred, and not only in physics. Body/mind dualism is as embedded in our thinking as the distinction between nouns and verbs. However, as we have seen, the processes of the mind actually shape the brain, and these physical changes in turn influence mental processes. The distinction between mind and brain becomes increasingly unclear. Although it is the "I" who thinks, the process of thinking necessarily depends upon the neurons and synapses and neurotransmitters of the brain. The process of thinking, while personal, is also electrochemical; it involves the brain. Yet the central focus is not upon the neurons, but upon what goes on *among* the neurons – their relationality.

So, we may be ready to move on to a new way of thinking about such distinctions. Whether we are thinking about the brain, or the Internet, or complexity, Plato's concept of form has largely been replaced by Claude Shannon's concept of *information*.[38] Information is the description of the way the world goes round: the shape assumed by substances, the sequence assumed by processes, and the interactions among substances and processes. Information is expressed as mathematical equations. But the equations are not the information. The information, like Plato's forms, is what is *embodied* in the substances and processes described by the equations.

Furthermore, there is an integral connection between these processes and complexity. Relationality, as we have seen, leads to complexification. The more integrated the relational processes, the more complex the entity. In some respects, then, descriptions of process and relationality provide us with our best insights into what is "really real." Much cutting-edge work is taking on the "flavour" of complexity and holism. In research from physics to economics, this work is aided by the formidable powers of computers, which allow for a great many variables to be considered at once. Our personal networks become ever more complex because electronic communication allows for the construction of more links than ever before among individuals and organizations. These links are active *in nature: they only assume reality through their relational process.*

These changes in understanding have major implications for Christian theology, according to Marjorie Hewitt Suchoki:

The structures that account for existence [may now be seen as] thoroughly relational, in keeping with the discoveries of physics. The import for Christian theology has been monumental with respect to the doctrine of God. If relationality, far from being an inferior accident of finite existence, is instead the sine qua non of all existence whatsoever, then the tension between God and the world is resolved. The question is not how a totally self-contained and self-sufficient reality can relate to anything outside of itself, but rather, how one can reinterpret creation, providence, redemption, and eschatology under the new relational paradigm.[39]

It would be a gross exaggeration to say that the conceptual boundaries between permanence and process are falling wholesale. Most of us separate them intuitively. We still get through our lives one step at a time. Much scientific work is still conducted piece by piece, in a more or less linear fashion. However, the two paradigm shifts are having their impact, for it now appears that the basic nature of things may be defined as much by process as by substance, and that the two are, at bottom, inseparable, even though we experience them differently on a practical level. One important impact of these shifts concerns our understanding of brain and mind.

# Chapter 2

---

# Character Development, Complexity and Holism

Let us turn now to an examination of ways in which these insights have affected our understanding of the human brain/mind. That human identity is not fixed but develops during a lifetime was seen by William James at the beginning of the twentieth century. He was followed by other analysts of character development, including Sigmund Freud, A.H. Maslow, Lawrence Kohlberg, and Erik Erikson. Brief references to their views, together with a longer discussion of James Fowler's study of spiritual growth, will help us relate that genre of thought to what we have already learned about complexification of character and holism.

## 2.1 Steps to Character Growth

### Some pioneers

For William James, an individual's integration of character was an achievement reached with effort over the course of a lifetime. He saw personality integration based on religious conviction as particularly valuable. Contemporaneously with James, Sigmund Freud in Vienna formulated childhood developmental stages within his psychoanalytic theory. Among adults, neurotics were of most interest to Freud. He believed their problems resulted from poor resolution of the central issues of some stage of childhood; different sorts of unresolved conflicts produced different neuroses. Religious belief was seen as akin to neurosis. However, rather like a priest, the analyst could help a patient resolve these "hang-ups" through the confessional "technology" of psychoanalysis; without the good offices of the analyst or his aides, people apparently had little chance of working through their problems. Freud's followers, including Carl Jung, forged other views. Although Jung's views would make an interesting study here, they require more development than this space allows.

### A.H. Maslow

As the twentieth century got well underway, more attention was paid to the characteristics of psychological health as opposed to illness, and to development in adulthood as well as in childhood. A.H. Maslow, unlike Freud, was most interested in the characteristics of psychologically healthy – and "superhealthy" – persons.[40] Maslow is known for his formulation of a hierarchy of needs that people work to satisfy. The "lower needs" are prioritized; once these are met, people turn to the satisfaction of the "higher" needs. Most basic are survival needs; once those are taken care of, one may concentrate on safety and security, and then on forging social ties. Next are needs for self-esteem and the respect of others. Those fortunate persons who have attained all the preliminary goals may work towards "self-actualization." A few people forge ahead towards self-actualization even though all their other needs have not entirely been met. Although persons at a self-actualized level have many characteristics in common, self-actualization for a given individual draws on that person's particular strengths; as these develop, new strengths are added and integrated. Although Maslow was agnostic, he was aware that deep personal change could take place rather abruptly, often in conjunction with religious or other ecstatic experiences. It appeared to him that such "peak experiences" are often correlated with progress towards self-actualization.[41]

### Lawrence Kohlberg

Another aspect of human character development concerns moral awareness. Pioneers in this field included Jean Piaget, who conceptualized stages of moral growth in children, and Lawrence Kohlberg, who studied moral development in both children and adults. Here we will pay particular attention to the work of Kohlberg, who found that people typically pass through stages of moral development in a predictable sequence, although not everyone progresses through all the stages. Kohlberg sketched the sequence as follows:

1. *The punishment and obedience orientation.*

> Avoidance of punishment and unquestioning deference to power are valued in their own right, not in terms of respect for an underlying moral order supported by punishment and authority.... At this stage the child is afraid of punishment. Fear generates his values.[42]

2. *The instrumental relativist orientation.*

Right action is characterized as

that which instrumentally satisfies one's own needs and occasionally the needs of others.... Reciprocity is a matter of "you scratch my back and I'll scratch yours," not of loyalty, gratitude or justice.[43]

3. *The "nice person" orientation.*

The approval of others is a central goal: Good behavior is that which pleases or helps others and is approved by them.... Behavior is frequently judged by intentions.[44]

4. *The law-and-order orientation.*

At this stage there is an

orientation towards authority, fixed rules and the maintenance of the social order. Right behavior consists in doing one's duty, showing respect for authority and maintaining the given social order for its own sake.[45]

Stage Four may very well be the stage that characterizes most adults in the United States and Canada.[46] Kohlberg identified three modalities through which Stage Four may develop, in a substage he called 4B. This substage has three possible orientations to what is behind the rules: (a) utility, or the welfare of the majority or of others, (b) the wishes, agreement, and viewpoint of the majority, and (c) the consensus of society's norms and beliefs, which may actually conflict with legal law or go beyond conventional obligations.[47] Persons who move from Stage Four to Stage Five develop skepticism towards the applicability of laws in all circumstances; this leads them to a degree of relativism. By moving to Stage Five, they allow for individual differences along with widespread agreement about certain norms.

5. *The social contract legalistic orientation.*

This orientation is embodied in the United States Constitution. Here,

right action tends to be defined in terms of general individual rights and in terms of standards which have been critically examined and agreed upon by the whole society. There is a clear awareness of the relativism of personal values and opinions and a corresponding emphasis upon procedural rules for reaching consensus. Aside from what is constitutionally and democratically agreed upon, the right is a matter of personal values and opinion.[48]

6. *The universal ethical principle orientation.*

Right is defined by the decision of conscience in accord with self-chosen ethical principles appealing to logical comprehensiveness, universality, and consistency. These principles are abstract and ethical (the Golden Rule, the categorical imperative), not concrete moral rules like the Ten Commandments.[49]

Ronald Duska and Mariellen Whelan, who write about these stages particularly as they apply to Roman Catholic moral education, point to the increasing individual responsibility assumed as persons pass through the stages of moral development. To this I would add that increasing integration and complexification can be perceived as a person grows through the stages of moral maturation. Concern is less exclusively directed to the self and more towards the social matrix; perception of subtleties of others' circumstances increases as well. Kohlberg's stages are not unrelated to stages of individual development proposed by Erik Erikson.

## Erik Erikson

Stages of development proposed by Erik Erikson focus upon the total personality. His original scheme involved eight stages,[50] but, as he and his wife, Joan, neared the age of 90, they perceived that a ninth stage should be added to address the issues of extreme old age.[51] Each stage includes a crisis, or challenge; the task is to meet that crisis so as to move on to the issues of the next stage. (Of course, this scheme does not entirely apply to the ninth stage, which ends in death.) Failure to solve a challenge results in a "characterological deviation" based on the unsolved conflict. The stages are as follows:

*1. Infancy:* Trust vs. mistrust. During infancy, basic trust in caretakers and the reliability of the world should be attained.

*2. Early childhood:* Autonomy vs. shame, doubt. The toddler's drive towards autonomy should be both guided and supported.

*3. Play age:* Initiative vs. guilt. Preschoolers' explorations and questions help them learn more about what kinds of persons they are going to be. If they are successful, initiative is supported.

*4. School age:* Industry vs. inferiority. School-age children wish to accomplish real tasks with competence and to gain a sense of mastery. Problems with such tasks may lead to a sense of inferiority.

*5. Adolescence:* Identity vs. identity diffusion. The teenager has a strong drive to establish ego identity. To find an identity, young people must convince themselves that success includes an effort to be the best.

*6. Young adulthood:* Intimacy vs. isolation. Personality integration enables persons to form intimate bonds. Along with bonding comes a need for discrimination and self-protection. In order to say yes to intimacy, one must be able to say no to people and forces that would threaten one's well-being.

*7. Adulthood:* Generativity vs. self-absorption. Generativity includes, importantly, efffective parenting, but also comprises mentoring and creative work. Those who do not develop generativity often sink into preoccupation with self-indulgence.

*8. Maturity:* Integrity vs. disgust, despair. This involves acceptance of one's own life, its trajectory and important relationships, along with acknowledgment that one's life is one's own responsibility.[52]

Matthew Arnold gives a flavour of this alternative in his 1852 poem "The Buried Life" (ll. 45 to 76):

> But often, in the din of strife
> There rises an unspeakable desire
> After the knowledge of the buried life;
> A thirst to spend our fire and restless force
> In tracking out our true, original course...

Yet still from time to time, vague and forlorn,
From the soul's subterranean depth upbourne

As from an infinitely distant land,
Come airs, and floating echoes, and convey
A melancholy into all our day.

*9. Old Age:* Dystonia vs. gerotranscendence. Joan Erikson, who wrote about this stage at the age of 93, did not give it a title; I have supplied that. The challenges of great age, she writes, reopen each of the previous crises. There are threats to trust, autonomy, initiative, industry, generativity, and integrity. Retaining the gains of a lifetime requires the marshalling of a lifetime's strengths. The antithesis to mistrust is hope; to shame and doubt, will; to guilt, purpose; to lack of industry, competence; to identity confusion, fidelity; to isolation, love; to stagnation, care; to despair, wisdom. Meeting such difficult challenges, day by day, may lead to a form of transcendence unique to very old age. Once again, in the Eriksons' work, we see a description of persons moving towards greater complexification, through integration of self and respectful, knowledgeable interaction with others.[53]

## *James W. Fowler*

Drawing upon the work of Erikson, Kohlberg and others, as well as his own research, James W. Fowler of Emory University focuses upon stages of faith development throughout the life cycle. These stages will be examined here in more detail than those of the other thinkers we have mentioned, not because they are necessarily superior to the other contributions, but because of their pertinence to the subject at hand. As we shall see, the stages delineated by Fowler describe an increase of complexity as expressed in the life of faith. Paradigm shifts in science in this postmodern era are thus reflected in Fowler's work – or perhaps it would be more accurate to say that Fowler is observing, and responding to, shifts in society's way of seeing "the way things really are." For purposes of this discussion, it is important to know that Fowler uses the term "faith" in a more inclusive sense than Christian, Buddhist, Islamic or Judaic faith, extending even beyond conventional religious faith. Understood in this more inclusive sense, faith may be characterized as:

>An integral, centering process, underlying the formation of the beliefs, values, and meanings that give coherence and direction to persons' lives;
>
>That links them in shared trusts and loyalties with others;
>
>That grounds their personal stances and communal loyalties in a sense of relatedness to a larger frame of reference; and
>
>That enables them to face and deal with the limit conditions of human life, relying upon that which has the quality of ultimacy in their lives.[54]

Fowler holds that faith, taken in this broader sense, is a common feature of human beings.

Like Erikson and Kohlberg, Fowler describes development in terms of stages; transitions between the stages involve challenge, upheaval and personality reorganization. In order to provide a quick overview of these stages, I provide here very short descriptions of each. Fowler's *Stages of Faith,* his best-known work, lists six stages.[55] However, in his most recent work, he inserts an additional stage at the beginning of the sequence.[56] Because the six-stage scheme is probably most familiar to readers, I will continue with this scheme; the additional stage will be termed the "pre-stage."

*Pre-Stage: Primal Faith* relates to basic trust. In the months of life before language develops, a disposition of trust forms through mutual relationships with parents and other caregivers. This basic trust helps to offset the anxiety and mistrust that an infant's normal disappointments tend to generate.[57]

*Stage 1: Intuitive-Projective Faith* is characteristic of young children at an age when they have many fantasies and learn by imitation. They can be powerfully and permanently influenced by examples, moods, actions and stories, including those related to the faith of their caregivers.[58]

*Stage 2: Mythic-Literal Faith* develops when children begin to take on for themselves the stories, beliefs and observances they learn in their faith community. Beliefs, moral rules and attitudes are taken quite literally.[59]

*Stage 3: Synthetic Conventional Faith* characterizes many young people and adults. At this stage, people tend to rely on authority and make commitments to particular values and images; "symbols and ritual representations expressive of [this] faith...are not separable from what they symbolize."[60] Such commitments can exert a powerful ordering effect upon personality.[61]

*Stage 4: Individuative-Reflective Faith* involves a relocation of authority from the external group to the self.[62] One must begin to take seriously the burden of responsibility for one's own commitments, lifestyle, beliefs and attitudes. One's roles and commitments to the faith community may remain important, but they no longer define reality.[63]

*Stage 5: Conjunctive Faith* involves a "willingness to let reality speak its word, regardless of the impact of that word on the security or self-esteem of the knower."[64] One "accepts as axiomatic that truth is more multidimensional and organically interdependent than most theories or accounts of truth can grasp."[65] Symbols of the faith once again become meaningful, but in a deeper way than before.[66]

*Stage 6: Universalizing Faith,* "heedless of...threats to self, to primary groups, and to institutional arrangements of the present order, becomes a disciplined activist incarnation...of the imperatives of absolute love and justice."[67] "Life is both loved and held to loosely."[68] Although greatness of commitment and vision often co-exist with great blind spots and limitations,[69] "trans-narcissistic love of human futurity" accounts for the readiness of these persons to "spend and be spent in making the Kingdom actual."[70] (Fowler and his colleagues have developed a questionnaire format to classify subjects by stage; this research instrument has been refined so that inter-interviewer agreement exceeds 90 per cent. It is important to note that Fowler and his colleagues have never encountered a "pure" example of Stage 6; they have, however, encountered persons who exemplified its characteristics in various ways.)

Each stage of faith is characteristically a complex, holistic way of perceiving and organizing life. But a person may reach a time when a particular stage of faith seems no longer adequate to circumstances and perceptions. After a period of turbulence, he or she may finally reorganize at a different, "higher" level. During such periods of transition, a person may combine some characteristics of one stage with some from another. But after a new stage is in place, one may look back on previous understandings with some chagrin. One may ask, Did I really think that? Didn't I know any better than that?

## 2.2 The Dynamics of Faith Development

What is the impetus behind this sort of personal reorganization? Usually a person is confronted with new challenges of one sort or another, either positive or negative. Perhaps tried and true relationships are no longer available. Perhaps new information leads to rethinking old opinions. Or new opportunities may open up, so that a person is able to make some important changes. There may be new experiences, additional responsibilities, new understandings; in order for the person to feel personally integrated, reorganization becomes necessary. And so the effort is made to weave more relationships, more thoughts and experiences into the persona. And this, in turn, may involve settling at a new faith stage.

Not everyone continues to move into new faith stages. In fact, many stabilize early on. Any faith stage beginning with the third is considered appropriate for an adult. Why do some people stabilize and others move on? Perhaps those who remain in one stage have had less challenging lives. Their circumstances and opportunities may simply be so stable that change is not forced; this may be especially true in traditional societies. If life is comfortable, and there is little need to change, only persons with a strong internal need for exploration and growth will make the effort to do so. For other people, to rethink established patterns and understandings may seem difficult, painful or risky. The payoff doesn't seem to be worth the pain; the challenge is too confusing. Unable to devise a way to deal with such challenges, the individual simply backs away. Sometimes, indeed, challenges are actively resisted and condemned, in much the same way that paradigm shifts in science are resisted by those invested in the old viewpoints. Such persons may become reactionary and regard most change as evil.

Everything that is new is not also good. Nor should everything old be scorned and discarded. A more complex stage not only comprises new learning, but also builds upon what has already been learned. Our "old" selves and our former understandings form part of the new synthesis. They are retained, but they form part of a larger and more complex grouping of understandings and responses. It is for this reason that religious persons may suddenly perceive new meanings in old beliefs. A passage of Scripture or a doctrine may be seen in a new light. Formerly puzzling teachings may suddenly make perfect sense. What once seemed restrictive may in fact become liberating.

Why do some people expand their personal scope, while others resist an expansion of their life experience and outlook? As we have seen, circumstances play an important role. The stimulus for change may not be there. In addition, any change has a cost as well as a benefit, and the price may simply be too high. But there is also another factor in play, and it presents an important application of what we have already seen: the values we have adopted, the ways we organize our thinking, shape the way we will integrate subsequent experiences, in both thought and action. What we believe now strongly influences what we will believe in the future. And in this way, the person we were has a lot to do with the person we are and will be. As John Milton observed in 1671,

> The childhood shows the man
> As morning shows the day.

> (*Paradise Regained,* Book IV, l. 220)

There is a related point to be made: the habitual traces of mind are tracked in the physical structure of the brain. Our mindset is reflected in our "brainset." We think our thoughts, but the brain does the work. Its neurons and synapses and neurotransmitters support, or fail to support, personal developments every step of the way. Fowler's stages of faith pertain to the development of the mind, but the implication is that they reflect developments in the brain as well. Yet, as we have seen, not all adults pass through all the stages. In fact, "persons may reach chronological and biological adulthood while remaining best defined by structural stages of faith that would most commonly be associated with early or middle childhood, or adolescence."[71] Why do some people proceed to more mature stages of faith development, while others do not? Let us trace the processes that are involved in the formation of each faith stage. We may thereby be able to deduce some answers to this question. As we do so, another pattern will emerge: as a person grows through the stages of faith, his or her personality seems to become more integrated and more complex.

### Primal Faith (Infancy)

In this first stage (which we have earlier called the "pre-stage" in order to preserve Fowler's familiar numeration of stages), a pre-language disposition of trust forms in the mutuality of one's relationships with parents and other caregivers. If this stage goes well, such basic trust will help to offset the anxiety and mistrust that inevitably affect the infant during the same period through experiences of separation and self-differentiation. Good care activates

> pre-potentiated capacities for finding coherence and reliability in self and primal others, for forming bonds of attachment with them, and for shaping a pre-disposition to trust the larger value and meaning commitments conveyed in parental care. Anxiety and mistrust have their own developmental pattern of emergence which caregivers' consistency and dependability help to offset.[72]

Thus, already in infancy, healthy development requires the infant to find coherence in self and to form bonds of attachment with others. Already the ground is laid for the young child to learn larger value and meaning commitments from significant others.

## 1. Intuitive-projective faith (Early childhood)

We see the emergence of a style of meaning-making based upon an emotional and perceptual ordering of experience.

> Imagination…responds to story, symbol, dream and experience…. Imagination…attempts to form images that can hold and order the mixture of feelings and impressions evoked by the child's encounters with the newness of both everyday reality and the penumbra of mystery that surrounds and pervades it…. [Y]oung children do not understand cause and effect relations well…. There is in this stage the possibility of aligning powerful religious symbols and images with deep feelings of terror and guilt, as well as of love and companionship. Such possibilities give this stage the potential for forming deep-going and long-lasting emotional and imaginal orientations – both for good and for ill.[73]

In other words, being a small child isn't always easy. The world is fraught with mystery. The efforts to make sense of things may lead a child to continually ask, Why? The alarming folk tales recorded by the Brothers Grimm, and today's scary tales by Maurice Sendak (for example, *In the Night Kitchen*) – not to mention J.K. Rowling's *Harry Potter* – only illustrate the child's clear sense of danger, chaos and mystery. Will the child feel it is possible to make sense of the world and triumph over chaos, as Harry Potter did? The conclusions drawn will set the style of future personality organization.

## 2. Mythic-Literal faith (Middle childhood and beyond)

By middle childhood, the brain has developed to the point that the child can grasp cause and effect. As a result, the young person can understand the world as a more sensible, predictable place, where events are relatively logical and prosaic. Narrative is now the main way of understanding symbols, and concepts are fairly concrete and literal. Concepts of ultimate reality focus on fairness and moral reciprocity. God is seen as a consistent, caring, but just ruler or parent. In this stage, goodness is rewarded; badness is punished.

Neither children nor adolescents nor adults of this stage carry out extensive analytic or synthetic reflection upon their stories. They offer narratives from the middle of the flowing streams of their lives. They do not "step out upon the banks" to reflect upon where the streams have come from, where they are going, or upon what larger meanings might give connection and integrated intelligibility to their collection of experiences and stories. ...the use of symbols and concepts remains largely concrete and literal.[74]

Here we see internal development building upon assumptions and orientations already begun in early childhood. The child is occupied with developing new abilities, learning schoolwork and household tasks, increasing skill and dominance in sports, forming clubs and cliques. Children who enjoy some success will develop feelings of mastery. But growth to a new stage then becomes necessary, because these very gains in experience and understanding may cast doubt on the assumptions of the Mythic-Literal stage: the child has learned that causes and effects are not always straightforward and just, and nice guys don't always finish first. The Mythic-Literal stage begins to wane with the discovery that ours is not always a "quick payoff world" with predictable rewards and punishments.

### 3. Synthetic-conventional faith (Adolescence and beyond)

Around the time of early adolescence, new connections develop in the maturing brain. They support the ability to use abstract concepts and also to see things in interpersonal perspective, so that other persons are known to have agendas and feelings separate from one's own. These developments open up new solutions to the injustices discovered towards the end of Stage Two. For example, God can be understood in terms of such personal qualities as accepting love, understanding, loyalty and support during times of crisis. Stage Three individuals "develop attachments to beliefs, values, and elements of personal style. They value qualities that link them...with the most significant others among their peers, family, and other non-family adults," and they depend upon these others for confirmation and clarity about their own identity and values. "Identity, beliefs, and values are strongly felt, even when they contain contradictory elements." An "ideology or worldview is lived and asserted" rather than reflected upon.[75] Many adults remain in Stage Three for the remainder of their lives. It can be a comforting and comfortable stopping point. Shared values and group support can make life seem worthwhile and cushion some of the difficulties that life brings. Threatening issues are held at bay.

Unresolved problems from earlier stages can prevent a person from reaching this stage, however. For example, if a person's concept of God reflects the punitive nature of a bad parent, thinking about spiritual issues may be avoided or actively rejected. As another example, if a person did not learn basic trust as an infant, then trust in any supportive group may not develop. A person who feels that life is more frightening than enjoyable might well decide to become a loner and to invest in others as little as possible. Thus, it is not unusual to find persons whose intellectual and practical life continues to complexify while their emotional life remains in a state of basic isolation, lacking in empathy or deep interaction with others.

By contrast, some adults not only reach Stage Three but eventually move on. This process probably has less to do with brain development than with exposure to a variety of ideas about the world. Comfortable assumptions may be challenged. Increased autonomy may demonstrate that in the end, the basic decisions about their lives rest with them. This may bring them to another crisis of belief, and finally to Stage Four.

## 4. Individuative-reflective faith (Young adulthood and beyond)

In order for this stage to emerge, two important movements must occur. "First, the previous stage's tacit systems of beliefs, values, and commitments must be critically examined.... Second, the self, previously constituted and sustained by its roles and relationships, must struggle with the question of identity and worth apart from its previously defining connections."[76] In the process, a person takes on for himself or herself the authority to determine and sanction goals and values. The definition of self no longer rests with one's reference group but with the self's new responsibilities to decide its roles and relations. Another change is that "the person becomes capable of third-person perspective, that is, of finding a standpoint for reflection that is set apart from the ebb and flow of events."[77] Through critical reflection the person now may "demythologize symbols, rituals, and myths."[78] Typically, their meanings are translated into conceptual formulations. "Frequently overconfident in their conscious awareness, persons of this stage attend minimally to unconscious factors that influence their judgment and behavior."[79] Stage Fours would agree with the well-known couplet

> I am the master of my fate,
> I am the captain of my soul.
> (William Ernest Henley, "Invictus")

In a sense, persons who move from Stage Three to Stage Four may seem to be decomplexifying. They demonstrate excessive confidence in conscious understanding and in critical thought, especially their own critical thought. In their focus on the "real," they may emphasize scientific realism, or the bottom line, or social research, or a system of thought built upon certain basic premises. However, there actually is increasing complexification in the move to Stage Four. Its focus is inward: an effort is being made to build a system of thought and decision-making that will promote the integration of the personal self. Not only do Stage Fours recognize their own autonomy, they are also cognizant of the autonomy of others. This is in contrast to Stage Three, where one's ideas reflect those of significant others, and the others, in turn, are perceived as being like oneself. Distinctions among persons are not very well defined at Stage Three, but at Stage Four, interpersonal boundaries are in place. Bonding with other individuals takes place across these clear boundaries.

Many people find Stage Four a good basis on which to reach equilibrium. Some, however, begin to see that there are mysteries beyond any intellectual framework that they may discover or construct, and that there are various paths to understanding. It may be threatening to leave the understandings of Stage Four, but some persons do move on to the next stage, Conjunctive Faith.

## 5. Conjunctive faith (Early midlife and beyond)

To leave Stage Four for the uncharted waters of Stage Five may require considerable courage. But some face the realization that *no* system of understanding can integrate all the realities of life. Rather,

> truth must be approached from a number of different directions and angles of vision.... In what Paul Ricoeur has called a "second" or a "willed naivete, persons of the Conjunctive stage manifest a readiness to enter the rich dwellings of meaning that true symbols, ritual and myth offer.[80]

There is rekindled interest in these symbols, but they are seen for what they are: suggestions of the nature of mysteries that lie beyond knowing. In this light their richness and import may be valued highly.

> The name of this stage implies a rejoining or a union of that which previously has been separated. The name comes from Nicolas of Cusa (1401–64), who wrote about what he called the *coincidentia oppositorium*, the "coincidence of opposites" in our apprehensions of truth.... We are many selves; we have a conscious mind, but we also are a great deal of patterned action and reaction that is largely unconscious. Those powerful and important unconscious aspects of selfhood are personal, social, cultural, and perhaps archetypal in origin. We are driven and pushed, as well as funded, from underneath by motives, desires, hungers – and lures of the spirit – which we have difficulty recognizing and integrating.[81]

Stage Five richly illustrates a central attribute of complexification: this stage clearly is played out at the cusp between order and disorder, between structure and freedom. Persons in Stage Five are ready to affirm some basic verities; at the same time, they bravely venture forth into uncharted depths, to see what may be found there.

Another hallmark of complexification also characterizes Stage Five: emergence. Many persons in this stage take unexpected turns in life. They may take on characteristics or projects or views that might not have been predicted on the basis of the personality previously evident. As they approach Stage Six, their courage seems to increase.

Fowler and his colleagues say they have never met a person who fully characterizes Stage Six. They have met persons who mix traits from Stage Five and Stage Six. To describe this final stage, they have synthesized traits observed in various people.

### 6. Universalizing faith (Midlife and beyond)

According to the ideal description of Stage Six, the

> structuring of this stage derives from the radical completion of a process of de-centration from self.... Each progressive stage marks a steady widening in social perspective taking. Gradually the circle of "those who count" in faith, meaning-making, and justice has expanded until, at the Conjunctive stage, it extends well beyond the bounds of social class, nationality, race, gender, ideological affinity, and religious tradition.... Psychodynamically, the self in this...stage moves beyond usual forms of defensiveness and exhibits an openness based on groundedness in the being, love, and regard of God.... Their approaches to personal and social reform are as concerned with the redemption and transformation of those they oppose as with bringing about justice and reform.[82]

They still have flaws – blind spots and inconsistencies – and their relations with others retain some old problems. But the person in Stage Six loves life dearly, even while holding on to life loosely. The central priority is no longer the survival of the self, but the advancement of the human project. Complexification has connected the person to the widest possible set of concerns, the deepest possible vision. Stage Six is, clearly, a rough equivalent of sainthood.

## 2.3 Faith Development, Complexification and Integration

Throughout this analysis, I have referred to the increasing complexification of character that accompanies personal growth through these faith stages. One characteristic of this development is growth in the scope of information available, whether more "book-learning" or more experience of how the world works. As people leave the home community, they tend to learn that vastly different customs, values and rules prevail in other groups. They see that violating the rules of childhood does not call down a thunderbolt from heaven, although there may be more subtle negative consequences. A person who gains more knowledge needs to integrate this knowledge in order for the world to make sense.

Also key is the increase of personal autonomy. As Kohlberg points out, one learns that one can in fact *decide* which rules to follow and how to live. In fact, one does decide, because even avoidance of decision is itself a decision. The responsibility and the consequences are both one's own to bear. Actions become more integrated as an individual takes ownership of them. As one recognizes one's own autonomy, one also recognizes the autonomy of the other. It becomes clear that many events in the world take their own course, and that one has no magical ability to control them.

Along with autonomy comes relationality. With better defined personality boundaries, relationships become more mature. Love is less a merger, more an interaction. The loved one is granted individuality and autonomy. The number of persons seen as significant grows beyond its earlier narrow definition. The circle widens.

Along with more clarity about what can and cannot be controlled may come greater tolerance of what is not known and perhaps cannot be known. The ambiguous becomes less threatening. Authority need not be invoked to provide an answer to every question.

With better boundaries between self and others, more clarity about the controllable and uncontrollable, and more tolerance of ambiguity, the complexifying person may become able to work within a structure that includes both order and chaos, and in fact may welcome the presence of both. For this cusp, we know, is the place that fosters further growth and creativity. With courage comes an increased exercise of freedom in moving towards what is deemed important. Progress in this quest gives rise to emergence. And so a developing personality may lay claim to new qualities.

Anywhere along the way, a person may pause and regroup. Perhaps complexification may resume, perhaps not. The process is effortful, and we human beings tend to avoid expending effort. However, we pay a price for failure to integrate. In fact, a case may be made that there is a relationship between complexification and virtue. Recall that Erikson and especially Kohlberg were concerned with growth in virtue. How might virtue and complexification be related?

### Complexity and virtue

Let us pause here to distinguish again between being complex and being complicated. People often say, "I need to simplify my life. My life is too complex. Simplicity is my goal." I think that what they mean, in the terminology employed here, is that their life is too complicated. Too complex it is not. A life (or another entity) that is complex is integrated. Its pieces work together in ways that are meaningful. Such a life is centred, and it has synergy. In a life that is complicated, though, there are lots of loose ends and unrelated pieces that play against each other. Such a person feels scattered. He or she should probably discard certain types of activity and concern, and try to integrate others. The etymology of the two words indicates that an "integrated" life will tend to have "integrity." It is this kind of life that can be called complex. Furthermore, a complexified life is characterized by emergence. A person whose energies are organized, whose powers are focused, tends to solve problems and invent novel solutions in vocational pursuits or personal relationships. A "scattered" person is less likely to do so.

Does complexification also have an impact upon virtue, as exemplified in personal behaviour? As cautionary examples, let us first consider persons whose lives are manifestly not well integrated. For example, highly impulsive persons may act on emotion with little regard for consequence. Lashing out in anger, quitting a job at the first insult, letting shyness lead to reclusiveness – we can all think of many examples of such behaviour, which is likely to have negative consequences. In fact, personality integration probably involves complexification of the neural circuitry as well. In the examples just cited, emotional impulses, which are linked with the brain's limbic system, are not sufficiently modified by consideration of outcomes – which involves the frontal lobes. As another example, consider the coldly analytic person who has little or no empathic feeling for others, but uses the left brain with skill. Persons who run intricate schemes of financial fraud that decimate others' retirement savings probably fall into this category. One can easily cite many other examples of unintegrated personality – and the havoc they wreak, to themselves and others. Abraham Maslow observed that rationality, emotion and the conative (wishing or driving) side of our nature are not necessarily in conflict, as some older theories maintained. Rather, "the healthy [person] is all of a piece, integrated, we might say. It is the neurotic person who is at odds with himself" or herself.[83] One is drawn back to Saint Paul's observations in the Letter to the Galatians: rather than "sorcery, enmities, strife, jealousy, anger, quarrels, dissensions, factions," and so on, we see in the integrated personality much more likelihood of "love, joy, peace, patience, kindness, generosity, faithfulness, gentleness, and self-control." (Galatians 5:20-21, 22-23, NRSV) When rationality, emotion and motivation work together, good things are more likely to happen.

Only a few of us have the opportunity, impetus, energy or courage to complexify as much as might be possible for us. As Saint Paul also observed, most of us fall short of the goal (cf. Romans 7:19).

# Chapter 3

# Personhood, the Imago Dei and the Deity

At this point it might be well to pause to consider where we have travelled so far, where our path of exploration has led, and where it might be taking us.

We began by exploring the ways in which natural or scientific understandings and social verities affect the way we human beings understand the world and our place in it. There are so many variables, and so many mysteries, that we need heuristic categories to help us come to grips with them. These categories are largely derived from our culture. To think about the Deity — far beyond the limits of the human mind — we must use analogies and metaphors drawn from our understandings, which naturally reflect the thinking of our particular era. We are not responsible for understanding ultimate truth because, with our human brain, we are not really capable of understanding it. We are responsible for understanding the truth as best we can in our time, and for doing what needs to be done at the time.

We have seen that two important shifts in understanding are unfolding in our own day. Understandings at the cutting edge, ways of thinking about "the way things really are," are becoming less linear and more weblike, more dependent on feedback and contingency. We are beginning to understand that systems can self-organize, with new and unexpected consequences, also known as emergent conditions. This process, called complexification, proceeds best in circumstances that provide a combination of predictability and freedom. Complexification is not linear — one thing does not necessarily lead to another in a straight-line progression. Instead, the interaction of many variables is involved. Nor is the outcome predetermined. It depends upon contingency as well as predictability, freedom as well as law.

A shift is also happening regarding distinctions between matter and energy, substance and process, brain and mind. While most of us keep these distinctions clear most of the time, in fact the boundaries are becoming increasingly blurred. At the farther reaches of science, this shift has been going on at least since 1905, when Einstein's Special Theory of Relativity showed that, in the realm of physics, matter and energy are interchangeable. Similarly, dualistic thinking about human nature is being modified.

The distinction between brain and mind is blurred by a cascade of new findings in neuroscience that is casting new light on human identity. Within the human brain, the processes of thought and observation and emotion and action strengthen neuronal pathways, thus altering both the structure and the function of the brain. These pathways help to determine our habitual modes of thought. However, we ourselves, by choosing our thoughts and our actions, can help to determine which neuronal pathways will be reinforced. Thus we see the influence of mind upon brain, as well as that of brain upon mind.

Rather than think about a dualism of substance and process, we may think in terms of information, which describes the way processes and substances are related and function. The mathematical formulas expressing information are not the actual information; that is imbedded within the very processes and substances being described. In these ways, we see a convergence in categories.

## 3.1 Personhood

How can we think of personhood within these new understandings? Is there in fact a difference between the person and the "stuff" that constitutes the person? These questions force us to take another look at the old problem of brain and mind. On the one hand, we have been discussing personal and spiritual growth in psychological and behavioural terms. Interspersed have been discussions of the brain and the ways in which it handles information. Although an overlap between the two has surely been implied, we have not addressed the issue head-on.

### Personhood and the mind/brain problem

In their recent book *What Makes Us Think?* Jean Changeux and Paul Ricoeur conduct a dialogue on issues of mind and body, as well as ethics and hope. Their dialogue revolves around study of the brain; as Ricoeur observes, this organ "remains the privileged site of conflicts between science and faith."[84] Neuroscientist Changeux, a nonbeliever, chaired the French National Advisory Committee on Bioethics from 1992 to 1998. Paul Ricoeur is a

French philosopher who operates within the ambience of Christian faith. In his view, religious belief – and the ultimate reality that underlies it – can provide a means to unleash the good. As these two thinkers come to grips with their disparities of viewpoint, they make important observations, which may help us to see in what directions our thoughts about human identity might proceed.

The first observation concerns interdisciplinary dialogue per se, especially the tendency for two disciplines to attach different meanings to the same word. For example, neuroscientists refer to emotions using medieval categories carried forward by Descartes and Spinoza – concepts such as pleasure, anger, distress and fear. But they describe these emotions in terms of neurotransmitters and cerebral geography. Meanwhile, a philosopher hears these same concepts complete with historical overtones. It is necessary to work at clarification of concepts, a sometimes tedious job that requires patience on both sides.

Second, it is important to be clear about the underlying science. Changeux lists five scientific advances that have altered this particular conversation significantly:[85]

1. *The understanding that anticipation and intention influence behaviour.* This insight represents a break with behaviourism, which focused on conditioned responses, not on the possibility of human freedom.

2. *Advances in neuropsychology,* which focuses on structural and functional relationships between the brain and particular psychological and/or behavioural functions (and dysfunctions).

3. *Brain imaging,* which links neural architecture with the dynamics of thought and the development of emotional states.

4. *Electrophysical experimentation,* in which, for example, sites in the brain are stimulated and subjects report the resulting experience.

5. *Work in brain chemistry,* which has yielded drugs to treat psychoses and mood disorders.

Third, it is important to recognize that there is no one-to-one overlay between science and our human experiences. Subjective experience has more complexity than scientific analysis can handle. As Ricoeur points out, there does not exist in the mind a replica of some external reality belonging to a wholly finished world.[86] Rather, we impose upon the world a mental and physical map that does not come ready-made. We learn "mapmaking" from our culture and experience and our own thinking. Awareness of self and "not-self" is one prerequisite to a useful mental map. To gain knowledge of the "not-self" requires interaction with other persons and nonhuman entities. The process of doing so involves various steps, including motivation to act, formulation of intentions, action, and assessment of outcomes. To speak only of the outcomes leaves out much of what is actually going on. This sort of analytical consideration is another critical component of interdisciplinary dialogue.

Changeux and Ricoeur have not solved the problem of brain and mind, nor will we. But our explorations, and their admonitions, do help to sharpen our focus on the issues.

### The human spirit

The subjective self functions beyond the scope of scientific analysis, Changeux and Ricoeur agree. It is sometimes discussed in terms of soul or spirit. People attach a multitude of connotations to these terms. These connotations include the mental (intentionality, meaning, mutual understanding) and the transcendental (the good, the just, the beautiful). Ricoeur would also include inspiration (enthusiasm, genius, religious feeling). Changeux, accusing Ricoeur of introducing teleology here (a great sin to scientific orthodoxy), would prefer instead a third level designated "conatus" – the joyous effort and striving of the creator – a suggestion that Ricoeur dismisses as scientific imperialism.[87] Many religious folk would also include an additional connotation: the essential core of a person that may in some form survive after death.

In this discussion of spirit, a dualistic way of thinking does survive, but with a twist. Changeux observes, "My brain does not think, but what I am thinking about always goes on in my brain."[88] If, in fact, the self has motivation and intention, forms itself, models the world, knows the "other," and experiences the transcendent, then it is also capable of ethical decision-making. It is in this freedom that the true reality of the self is demonstrated. The self is responsible for understanding what can be understood and doing what needs to be done at the time. And the self is closely related to what we think of as the mind.

Nonetheless, the self, at least as we know it in this life, is always embodied. Its embodiment is part of its selfhood. And conversely, the self – the mind – has choices to make, and to some extent it shapes its own embodiment. And so the mind/body relationship in some respects reflects what we have seen about complexity. Freedom and choice are part of the picture, but so are lawfulness and predictability, because various kinds of activities operate dependably in both the brain and the rest of the body. Thus, we human beings are situated on that very cusp that gives rise to creativity and newness and complexification: the border between order and freedom. And these may give rise to spiritual development.

### The role of religion

Do religious tradition and praxis have a role vis á vis the spirit? Indeed, they should help people to understand what can be understood about themselves, the world and the transcendent, and to make judgments about what needs to be done at the time. Importantly, they should help people to distinguish between what is custom and what is of central importance. (For example, it is not necessary to decorate the Christmas tree, but for Christians, it is necessary to recognize the Christmas event's central message.)

Central to these responsibilities of religion is myth which, according to Ricoeur, is a way of wrestling with enigma.[89] *Myth,* as used here, refers to the central narratives of religious belief, not to fairy tales. Myth is a way to express the deep kinds of truth and wisdom that are almost inexpressible. Myth makes central truths accessible through narrative, an essential human way of knowing that is common to all cultures. How we understand various myths, and how we act upon them, depends not only on our particular personal and cultural background, but also upon the stage of faith that we ourselves have reached.

What conclusions about the role of religion might one draw from the work of Changeux and Ricoeur and our reflections here? First, if religions are to help people to distinguish what is of central importance, then it may well be the responsibility of religious leaders to encourage people to mature from one stage of complexity to another. Religious leaders should not try too hard to keep people in a "safe" holding pattern at a middling stage of complexification. In fact, this seems to have been one goal of decisions made at Vatican Council II, which stated explicitly,

> Authentic freedom is an exceptional sign of the divine image within man. For God has willed that man be left "in the hand of his own counsel" (Sir. 15:4) so that he can seek his creator spontaneously and come freely to utter and blissful perfection through loyalty to him. Hence, man's dignity demands that he act according to a knowing and free choice. Such a choice is personally motivated and prompted from within. It does not result from blind internal impulse or from mere external pressure.[90]

Furthermore, such a responsibility would mean that religious leaders should themselves be selected partly on the basis of their own capacity to mature spiritually, and that they should be supported in their own struggles for maturation.

This approach requires courage. It is not reckless, though, because faith is based on "a fundamental approval which comes from somewhere farther away and higher than I am, in my courage to live and to make goodness prevail over the evil whose radicality I have both lamented and accepted," suggests Ricoeur, echoing Paul Tillich.[91] Such faith, along with hope and courage, is critical to the task. In the fifth century BCE, Heraclitus observed, "If you do not hope the unhoped for, you will not find."[92] Let us hope for religious praxis that encourages and embodies spiritual growth.

## 3.2 The Imago Dei

So far, we have traced some challenges to dualistic thinking, and some ideas about complexification and emergence. These ideas are influencing the scientific thinking of our time. We have examined some ways in which they may also affect our concepts of human nature, and their relationship to the process of spiritual growth.

Now we will dramatically shift the focus of our inquiry. If these ideas influence our understandings of the world and of human nature, might they also have a bearing on our concepts of God? As we saw in the opening section of this book, human beings' ideas about the Deity have always been coloured by the thought forms of their time. Ideas about God have unfolded as people have lived through a succession of historical epochs.

The question of the God concept gains immediacy because the Judeo-Christian Scriptures teach that we human beings have been created in the Image of God. Thus, our ideas about God may also affect our ideas about ourselves or, if not about our actual selves, then about the high potential for which a person may strive, and the ways in which one might go about doing this. So let us see what difference these latest paradigms might make for our understanding of what it might mean to have been created in the Image of God.

### Biblical understandings

To begin, let us examine the biblical roots of the concept of the Imago Dei. A great deal has been made of a few verses in the first chapter of Genesis. According to this account, after the animals had been created,

> God said, "Let us make humankind in our image, according to our likeness; and let them have dominion over the fish of the sea, and over the birds of the air, and over the cattle, and over all the wild animals of the earth, and over every creeping thing that creeps upon the earth." So God created humankind in his image, in the image of God he created them, male and female he created them. (Genesis 1:26-27)

Note that in this account the male and female were created at the same time. It is a matter of debate whether reference to the first humans implies one first pair or the human species, *Homo sapiens sapiens*. (The use of the plural in the first sentence is often interpreted to refer to the "divine retinue," or the Trinity, rather than to plural gods.)

The New Testament contains another well-known reference to the Image of God. Here Christ is described as

> the image of the invisible God, the firstborn of all creation; for in him all things in heaven and on earth were created, things visible and invisible, whether thrones or dominions or rulers or powers – all things have been created through him and for him. (Colossians 1:15-16.)

Although both Christ and other humans reflect the Image of God, clearly Christ ranks on a different level: he is the firstborn; all things have been created through him and for him. In both these passages, however, embodied beings are presented as images of a God who is mysterious, invisible, beyond comprehension. Perhaps this is so because we humans need an embodied way to think about the nature of the Deity. We need to see, smell, touch, in order to feel that we know.

## Anthropomorphism and natural theology

Since the time of Ludwig Feuerbach at the turn of the nineteenth century, cognoscenti have tended to dismiss this kind of God-talk as anthropomorphism – inventing a god in the image of man. That accusation is often valid. People do think of God in terms of human ideals, whether those include the good parent, the lover, the friend, the jealous, wrathful tyrant, the just ruler – the list is long. We often project our longings for love and safety, or for punishment and limits, onto a deity designed for our personal satisfaction.

However, there may be another way to think about the issue. Knowledge and insights gained over our lifetimes and by persons who have come before us can add dimensions to this conversation that may be helpful to us in our particular time. These certainly include personal insights; less expectedly, they may also include scientific knowledge. What if we enrich this exploration with our knowledge that we humans co-evolved with our natural setting? We now know, or believe, that we are part of the strange universe of quarks and leptons, of ions and molecules, of carbon-based life, of the prokaryotic and eukaryotic lines within which living things evolved. In a scientific sense, we do not know the answer to the central question: Why is there something rather than nothing? And yet, those of us who believe in God believe that a foundational power is behind this strange and wonderful universe and is intricately involved with it. And so, it follows that the nature of the universe must in some way track and reflect the image of the power that created it.

I have edited a large number of books, and by the time I have spent hours of intensive work on a manuscript, I have a deep sense of the character of the writer. Even if I have never met the author, and the work is not autobiographical, I still know a lot about how that person operates. Similarly, the author of the universe must, I believe, have left imprints all over the universe story, and from them, we can discern something of the author's character. This may be a version of natural theology that is appropriate for our time.

The present exploration points to a God who is infinitely complex – that is, who is meaningfully connected to all that is, and who brings all together into a meaningful whole. This is a God who includes and transcends all information, if information is seen as description of all that is and all that happens. "All that is" may be seen as representing the *substance* of all, and "all that happens" as representing the *process* of all. Process and substance, as these terms are commonly used today, denote realities that are not separate, but two aspects of the same reality. In the metaphor of grammar, we might say God is manifested as both a noun and a verb! Such a God is not static, but infinitely interactive in dealings with the universe.

Because the mind/brain is also capable of interaction and complexification, it is capable of a relationship with such a God. Such a relationship would then be reliable, like the natural laws that uphold our existence. At the same time, the relationship would be dynamic and interactive. Humans have enough freedom to participate in such a dynamic interrelationship.

It is certainly self-centred of us humans to believe we are the best thing that ever happened to the world and that we must therefore reflect the Image of God more clearly than anything else that has emerged. With some trepidation, nevertheless, I point out that the human brain is the most complex entity, for its size, that we know of in the universe. In addition, complexification does seem to be one of the built-in processes that centrally characterize "the way things really are." And so, if the power behind the universe is what we call God, and if the trend towards complexification is one of the bottom-line characteristics of the universe, and if human beings are among the most complex things around, then it is only a small stretch of reasoning to conclude that perhaps human beings do indeed in some respects reflect the Image of God. And to the degree that we continue to complexify and to grow spiritually, we may reflect that image more fully.

## Evil and the Imago Dei

Yes, of course, the issue of theodicy raises its troubling challenge at this point. Humans can be exceedingly evil – does that, too, reflect the Image of God? To echo a character who appears early in Archibald MacLeish's poem/play *J.B.,*

> If God is God he is not good.
> If God is good he is not God.
> Take the even, take the odd.
>
> (Archibald MacLeish, *J.B.*)

In response to this challenge, let us back up to what we have learned about complexification. What are the requisite conditions for complexification to occur? Some dependable laws, some order, and also some contingency, some freedom. In order for human beings, or anything else, to complexify, some freedom has to be included in the mix. That seems to be the way the universe works. So the dilemma that MacLeish poses to our understanding of God is a forced choice that does not reflect the real alternatives. The choices may in fact lie among the following:

1. *An extreme of control,* in which there would not be room for human evil, but there would also be no potential for human complexification and spiritual growth (humanity as we know it could not exist under these conditions),

2. *A combination of freedom and order,* in which complexification could occur – as could evil, and

3. *Complete lack of order,* in which there would be no basis for action, and there could be no life, as we saw in our discussion of the endpoint of entropy.

At this point in the history of the universe, the second option is clearly in effect. This arrangement allows for change – not only the negative "change and decay" but also, and more desirably, change and development and richness of life.

And so, it may be that human beings reflect the Image of God to the extent that we opt for complexification, for richness of life, for progression through the various stages of faith. It may be necessary to choose such an option even when God seems hidden and we figuratively, spiritually, stand at the edge of the abyss. Yet, as Vatican II noted, even when God seems hidden one should not choose to remain "risk-free," in a holding pattern. Rather, one should dare to venture into discipleship as it beckons, into callings as they are discerned. To be sure, there is also that level of order and predictability that must be respected in the pattern of creation. This must be nurtured. But it ought not put an end to our story by imposing a paralysis.

### One view of sainthood

It is instructive to consider here those few persons who reach Stage Six of Fowler's stages of faith. Although they are exceedingly rare, we may learn from some who may have been at or near that level. Abraham Lincoln of Illinois may have been an example. When Lincoln arrived in Washington, many thought him simple. But he was not; his writings reveal a highly complex intellect that was focused upon an increasingly organized and transcendent vision of the society and his role in it. Lincoln continued to complexify in office and to deepen in spiritual insight. His reward for freeing the slaves in the United States, by means of the Emancipation Proclamation, was to be shot dead by John Wilkes Booth. The assassination occurred on April 14, 1865 – coincidentally, Good Friday. Other examples of persons who no doubt reached Stage Six are Mother Teresa and Albert Schweitzer, who were at times prickly personalities. We are well aware that Schweitzer had to work hard to integrate the disparate pieces of his character. Although their lives had a devotional dimension, none of these persons spent all their time in mystical contemplation. They also employed reflection, emotional commitment, logical analysis, future planning and action. They built solid relationships with those around them – otherwise we would never have heard of them. The solitary mystic who seldom connects with others is less likely to be remembered through the centuries. I submit that the lives of Stage Six heroes and heroines were complexified, and that this complexity issued in something that we might describe as virtue. They confronted evil and dared the abyss. Despite their many flaws, they may still provide us with the best human examples of the Image of God, except for Jesus himself, who, as Saint Paul makes clear in his Letter to the Colossians, was quite another sort of being.

## 3.3 Glimpses of the Deity

Might our insights about complexity and holism, about the fuzzy boundaries between matter and energy, process and substance, enable us to catch some new glimpses of the force behind the universe whom we call God? For centuries, the "personality" of this being has proven quicksilvery and elusive. In the early centuries CE, a series of Councils worked towards a Trinitarian understanding that has been formalized in the Nicene Creed. The Holy Spirit was described as "the Lord and Giver of Life, who proceedeth from the Father and the Son" (in the Orthodox tradition, "Who proceedeth from the Father"). The word "proceed" is derived from the Latin *procedo,* which is also the root of our word "process." To the extent that Trinitarian doctrine expresses human experiences of the divine nature, it would seem that the Spirit, in particular, expresses the experience of the dynamic nature of the Deity. Saint Augustine, who was familiar with the marine life of the Mediterranean, described the earth and God with the metaphor of the sponge and the sea. The world as we know it is like a submerged sponge. God is the ever-changing sea, which penetrates the sponge, supports the sponge, nourishes the sponge and gives it life – but is not itself the sponge. As long as the sea flows through the sponge, the sponge may remain alive. Thus, in this metaphor, God is forever interacting with the world, yet God is not the world. Like the sea, God is dynamic and mysterious, always the same, yet never the same; God's very being may be experienced as action and interaction.[93]

God as process may be known directly; God as substance may never be known in such a way, although intellect and tradition may infer God as substance. As Joseph Bracken points out, "God as an empirically verifiable entity is simply not available to experience…. All that the 'believer' and 'nonbeliever' alike experience is an activity" – a hidden creativity at work in the historico-cultural process and "an ultimate tendency or power, which is working itself out in nature and human history."[94] Bracken adds, however, that "the full entitive reality of God…can be discerned through prayer and reflection on the text of Scripture."[95]

Our new insights teach us to see life in terms of process. The state of any life form is always flux; as long as it remains dynamic, the entity remains alive. When dynamism stops, when homeostasis ceases to function, life stops as well. The Lord, the Giver of Life may not only be experienced but may also be understood as process. A dynamic model of a God in continual interaction with the world may be fruitful for our day. To exist in the Image of God may then mean to live in continual responsiveness to the callings that are ours in particular, doing what needs to be done at the time.

During this twenty-first century, we humans may manage to destroy ourselves and our ecosystem or our supportive culture and our "social capital" through mistaken and evil choices. But if not, by the end of this century some of the things being said now will seem as prophetic as the words of William James in 1902. And there will also be new insights and new paradigms. They will bring to us new metaphors by which we can try to grasp the unknowable, new ways in which the ancient myths can cast light on the puzzles and dilemmas of the people who live at the turn of the twenty-second century. For now, we make do with what we have. And that is all that is required – for now.

Yet, because we necessarily perceive and think with our brain – which, though complex, is still very human – we continue to look for cause and effect, for understandings of the basic nature of our world, the fundamental meaning of our lives, in thought forms that make sense to us. We can only glimpse an Image of God "through a glass darkly," illuminated by "small lights." For these lights we are thankful:

We thank Thee for the lights that we have kindled,
The light of altar and of sanctuary;
Small lights of those who meditate at midnight
And lights directed through the coloured panes of windows
And light reflected from the polished stone,
The gilded carven wood, the coloured fresco.
Our gaze is submarine, our eyes look upward
And see the light that fractures through unquiet water.
We see the light but see not whence it comes.
O Light Invisible, we glorify Thee!
> In our rhythm of earthly life we tire of light. We are
> glad when the day ends, when the play ends;
>> and ecstasy is too much pain.
We are children quickly tired: children who are up in the
night and fall asleep as the rocket is fired; and the
day is long for work or play.
We tire of distraction or concentration, we sleep and are
glad to sleep,
Controlled by the rhythm of blood and the day and the
night and the seasons.
And we must extinguish the candle, put out the light and
relight it;
Forever must quench, forever relight the flame.
Therefore we thank Thee for our little light, that is dappled
with shadow.
We thank Thee who has moved us to building, to finding,
to forming at the ends of our fingers and beams of
our eyes.

And when we have built an altar to the Invisible Light, we
may set thereon the little lights for which our bodily
vision is made.
And we thank Thee that darkness reminds us of light.
O Light Invisible, we give Thee thanks for Thy great glory!

(T.S. Eliot, "Choruses from "The Rock," X, ll. 26–46)

# Notes

[1] John Hedley Brooke, *Science and Religion: Some Historical Perspectives* (Cambridge: Cambridge University Press, 1991), 61.

[2] Michael Polanyi, *Personal Knowledge: Towards a Postcritical Philosophy* (New York: Harper Torchbooks, 1964), cited in Bracken, Joseph A., S.J., "Panentheism from a Process Perspective, " in *Trinity in Process: A Relational Theology of God,* ed. Joseph A. Bracken, S.J., and Marjorie Hewitt Suchocki (New York: Continuum, 1997), 109.

[3] Immanel Kant, *The Critique of Pure Reason.* In *Great Books of the Western World*, vol. 42, *Kant.* (Chicago: Encyclopedia Britannica [1781] 1952).

[4] Miguel de Unamuno (n.d.). Cited in *Discover,* Sep. 2001, 18.

[5] Mariano Artigas, *The Mind of the Universe: Understanding Science and Religion* (Radnor, PA: Templeton Foundation Press, 1999), 193.

[6] See Mariano Artigas, *The Mind of the Universe,* 193.

[7] Thomas Kuhn, *The Structure of Scientific Revolutions.* 2d enlarged ed. (Chicago: University of Chicago Press, 1970).

[8] Philip P. Wiener, ed., *Dictionary of the History of Ideas: Studies of Selected Pivotal Ideas*, vol. 2, 113, s.v. Entropy.

[9] Ibid., 179, s.v. Evolutionism.

[10] Murray Gell-Man, *The Quark and the Jaguar: Adventures in the Simple and Complex* (New York: W.H. Freeman, 1994), passim.

[11] Paul Davies, "The Unreasonable Effectiveness of Science." In *Evidence of Purpose: Scientists Discover the Creator*, ed. John Marks Templeton (New York: Continuum, 1994), 119.

[12] Lynn Margulis, *Origin of Eucaryotic Cells* (New Haven: Yale University Press, 1970). Cited in Freeman Dyson, *Origins of Life,* rev. ed. (Cambridge: Cambridge University Press), 15.

[13] Freeman Dyson, *Origins of Life,* 15. See also Lynn Margulis, *Symbiosis in Cell Evolution* (San Francisco: Freeman, 1981), and Christian deDuve, *Vital Dust: The Origin and Evolution of Life on Earth* (New York: Basic Books, 1995).

[14] Peter Coveney and Roger Highfield, *Frontiers of Complexity: The Search for Order in a Chaotic World* (New York: Fawcett Columbine, 1995), 214.

[15] Ibid., 285.

[16] Merlin Donald, *A Mind So Rare: The Evolution of Human Consciousness* (New York: W.W. Norton, 2001), 101–3.

[17] Floyd E. Bloom and Arlyne Lazerson, *Brain, Mind, and Behavior,* 2d ed. (New York: W.H. Freeman, 1988), 31.

[18] Marian Cleeves Diamond. *Enriching Heredity: The Impact of the Environment on the Anatomy of the Brain* (New York: The Free Press, 1988), 91–114.

[19] See Michael Specter, "Rethinking the Brain," Annals of Science, *The New Yorker,* July 23, 42–53, and David Kornack and Pasko Rakic, "No Evidence of New Neurons in Adult Primate Neocortex," UniSci – Daily University Science News, <http://unisci.com/stories/20014/120704.htm>, Dec. 7, 2001.

[20] Specter, "Rethinking the Brain," 48.

[21] Antonio Damasio, *The Feeling of What Happens: Body and Emotion in the Making of Consciousness* (New York: Harcourt Brace, 199), 23–24.

[22] Francis Crick, *The Astonishing Hypothesis: The Scientific Search for the Soul* (New York: Simon & Schuster, 1994), 3.

[23] Roger Sperry, "Paradigms of Belief: Theory and Metatheory," *Zygon: Journal of Religion and Science* 26 (June 1992): 237–58.

[24] George Ellis, "Reductionism," *Metaviews* 002, January 26, 2000, <metaviews@META-LIST.ORG>.

[25] William James, *The Varieties of Religious Experience* (New York: Simon & Schuster, [1902] 1997), 146.

[26] William James, *The Varieties of Religious Experience,* 149–50.

[27] R. McSherry, E. M. Ciulla, S. Salisbury, and D. Tsuang, *Social Compass* 35 (1987), 4: 515–37.

[28] Harold G. Koenig et al., *International Journal of Psychiatry in Medicine* 27 (1997): 233–50.

[29] J. I. Kark et al., *American Journal of Public Health* 86 (1996): 341–46.

[30] D. Oman and D. Reed, *Americanb Journal of Public Health* 88 (1998): 1469–75.

[31] Harold G. Koenig, K. Pargament, and J. Nielsen, *Journal of Nervous and Mental Disease* 186 (1998): 513–52.

[32] Philip P. Wiener, ed., *Dictionary of the History of Ideas,* vol. 2 (New York: Charles Scribner's Sons, 1973), 39–40.

[33] Frank Thilly, rev. by Ledger Wood, *A History of Philosophy.* (New York: Henry Holt, 1952), 80.

[34] Frank Tilly, rev. by Ledger Wood, *A History of Philisophy*, 83.

[35] Frank Thilly, rev. by Ledger Wood, *A History of Philosophy,* 307.

[36] Marjorie Hewitt Suchocki, "Introduction," in Joseph A. Bracken, S. J., and Marjorie Hewitt Suchocki, eds.,*Trinity in Process: A Relational Theology of God* (New York: Continuum, 1997), vii.

[37] Frank Thilly, rev. by Ledger Wood, *A History of Philosophy,* 309.

[38] Claude Shannon and Warren Weaver, *The Mathematical Theory of Communication* (Urbana: University of Illinois Press, 1949).

[39] Marjorie Hewitt Suchocki, "Introduction," viii.

[40] See A.H. Maslow, *Motivation and Personality,* 2d ed. (New York: Harper & Row, 1970).

[41] A.H. Maslow, *Religions, Values, and Peak-Experiences* (Columbus: Ohio State University Press, 1964). See also Appendix A, "Comments on 'Religions, Values, and Peak-Experiences,'" in A.H. Maslow, *The Farther Reaches of Human Nature* (New York: Viking, 1971), 343–50.

[42] Ronald Duska and Mariellen Whelan, *Moral Development: A Guide to Piaget and Kohlberg* (New York: Paulist, 1975), 53.

[43] Ibid., 55.

[44] Ibid., 61.

[45] Ibid., 65.

[46] Ibid., 64–65.

[47] Ibid., 67.

[48] Ibid., 73–74.

[49] Ibid., 76.

[50] Erik H. Erikson, *Identity and the Life Cycle* (New York: W.W. Norton, [1959] 1980).

[51] See Erik H. Erikson and Joan M. Erikson, *The Life Cycle Completed.* Extended Version with New Chapters on the Ninth Stage of Development (New York: W.W. Norton, 1997).

[52] Erikson H. Erikson, *Identity and the Life Cycle,* 100–103.

[53] Erik H. Erikson and Joan M. Erikson, *The Life Cycle Completed.*

[54] James W. Fowler, *Stages of Faith* (San Francisco: HarperSanFrancisco, [1981] 1995), 1.

[55] James W. Fowler, *Stages of Faith.*

[56] James W. Fowler, "Stages of Faith and the Human Brain: Can Neuroscience Illumine the Path Towards Universalizing Faith?" Paper presented at the Montreal CTNS Advanced Workshop "Neuroscience, Religious Experience and the Self," May 31–June 5, 2001.

[57] Ibid., 3.

[58] James W. Fowler, *Stages of Faith,* 133.

[59] Ibid., 149.

[60] Ibid., 162–63.

[61] Ibid., 154.

[62] Ibid., 179.

[63] Ibid., 181.

[64] Ibid., 185.

[65] Ibid., 186.

[66] Ibid., 197.

[67] Ibid., 200.

[68] Ibid., 202.

[69] Ibid., 201–202.

[70] Ibid., 211.

[71] James W. Fowler, "Stages of Faith and the Human Brain," 2.

[72] Ibid., 2.

[73] Ibid., 3.

[74] Ibid., 3.

[75] Ibid., 5.

[76] Ibid.

[77] Ibid.

[78] Ibid.

[79] James W. Fowler, *Stages of Faith,* 179–80.

[80] James W. Fowler, "Stages of Faith and the Human Brain," 5.

[81] Ibid., 7.

[82] James W. Fowler, "Stages of Faith and the Human Brain," 6–7.

[83] A.H. Maslow, *Motivation and Personality,* 271.

[84] Jean Changeux and Paul Ricoeur, *What Makes Us Think?* Princeton, NJ: Princeton University Press, 2000), 169.

[85] Ibid., 48–61.

[86] Ibid., 72.

[87] Ibid., 177.

[88] Ibid., 40.

[89] Ibid., 288.

[90] Walter M. Abbot, S.J., ed., *The Documents of Vatican II* (America Press, 1955), 214, cited in Ronald Duska and Mariellen Whelan, *Moral Development,* 90–91.

[91] Ibid., 286.

[92] Jean Changeux and Paul Ricoeur, *What Makes Us Think?* 303.

[93] St. Augustine, *Confessions,* Bk. VII, V, 7.

[94] Joseph A. Bracken, S.J., "Panentheism from a Process Perspective," in Joseph A. Bracken, S.J., and Marjorie Hewitt Suchocki, eds., *Trinity in Process: A Relational Theology of God* (New York: Continuum, 1997), 108, in reference to Gordon Kaufman, *Theology for a Nuclear Age* (Philadelphia: Westminster, 1985), 42.

[95] Joseph A. Bracken, S.J., "Panentheism from a Process Perspective," 108.

# Bibliography

Artigas, M. (1999). *The Mind of the Universe: Understanding Science and Religion.* Radnor, PA.: Templeton Foundation Press.

Ashbrook, J.B., and Albright, C.R. (1997). *The Humanizing Brain: Where Religion and Neuroscience Meet.* Cleveland: Pilgrim.

———. (2001). *Where God Lives in the Human Brain.* Naperville, IL: Sourcebooks.

Augustine, St. ([ca. 400] 1952). *Confessions.* In *Great Books of the Western World*, vol. 18, *Augustine* Chicago: Encyclopedia Britannica.

Bracken, J.A., S.J. (1997). "Panentheism from a Process Perspective." In *Trinity in Process: A Relational Theology of God,* ed. Joseph A. Bracken, S.J., and Marjorie Hewitt Suchocki. New York: Continuum.

Brooke, J.H. (1991). *Science and Religion: Some Historical Perspectives.* Cambridge: Cambridge University Press.

Changeux, J-P, and Ricoeur, P. (2000). *What Makes Us Think?* Princeton, NJ: Princeton University Press.

Coveney, P., and Highfield, R. (1995). *Frontiers of Complexity: The Search for Order in a Chaotic World.* New York: Fawcett Columbine.

Crick, F. (1994). *The Astonishing Hypothesis: The Scientific Search for the Soul.* New York: Simon & Schuster.

Damasio, A. (1994). *Descartes' Error: Emotion, Reason, and the Human Brain.* New York: G.P. Putnam.

———. (1999). *The Feeling of What Happens: Body and Emotion in the Making of Consciousness.* New York: Harcourt Brace.

Davies, P. (1994). "The Unreasonable Effectiveness of Science." In *Evidence of Purpose: Scientists Discover the Creator,* ed. John Marks Templeton. New York: Continuum.

de Duve, C. (1995). *Vital Dust: The Origin and Evolution of Life on Earth.* New York: Basic Books.

Diamond, M.C. (1998). *Enriching Heredity: The Impact of the Environment on the Anatomy of the Brain.* New York: The Free Press.

Donald, M. (2001). *A Mind So Rare: The Evolution of Human Consciousness.* New York: W.W. Norton.

Duska, R., and Whelan, M. (1975). *Moral Development: A Guide to Piaget and Kohlberg.* New York: Paulist.

Dyson, F. (1999). *Origins of Life.* Rev. ed. Cambridge: Cambridge University Press.

Eliot, T.S. ([1925] 1952). *The Complete Poems and Plays 1909–1950.* New York: Harcourt Brace.

Ellis, G. (2000). "Reductionism." *Metaviews* 002, January 26. <metaviews@META-LIST.ORG> [archived listserv]

Erikson, E.H. ([1959] 1980). *Identity and the Life Cycle.* New York: W.W. Norton.

────── and Erikson, J.M. 1997. *The Life Cycle Completed.* Extended Version with New Chapters on the Ninth Stage of Development. New York: W.W. Norton.

Fowler, J.W. ([1981] 1995). *Stages of Faith.* San Francisco: HarperSanFrancisco.

──────. (2001). "Stages of Faith and the Human Brain: Can Neuroscience Illumine the Path Towards Universalizing Faith?" Paper presented at the Montreal CTNS Advanced Workshop "Neuroscience, Religious Experience and the Self," May 31–June 5, 2001.

Gell-Mann, M. (1994). *The Quark and the Jaguar: Adventures in the Simple and Complex.* New York: W.H. Freeman.

Haught, J.F. (2000). *God After Darwin: A Theology of Evolution.* Boulder, CO: Westview.

Holland, J.H. (1998). *Emergence.* Reading, MA: Perseus.

James, W. ([1902] 1997). *The Varieties of Religious Experience.* New York: Simon & Schuster.

Kant, I. ([1781] 1952). *The Critique of Pure Reason.* In Great Books of the Western World, vol. 42, Kant. Chicago: Encyclopedia Britannica.

Kark, J.I., et al. (1996). *American Journal of Public Health* 86: 341–46.

Kauffman, S. (1995). *At Home in the Universe: The Search for Laws of Self-Organization and Complexity.* New York: Oxford University Press.

Kaufman, G. (1985). *Theology for a Nuclear Age.* Philadelphia: Westminster.

Koenig, H.G., et al. (1997). *International Journal of Psychiatry in Medicine* 27: 233–50.

———., Pargament, K., and Nielsen, J. *Journal of Nervous and Mental Disease* 186: 513–52.

Kuhn, T.S. (1970). *The Structure of Scientific Revolutions.* second enlarged ed. Chicago: University of Chicago Press.

MacLeish, A. (1958). *J.B.: A Play in Verse.* Boston: Houghton Mifflin.

Margulis, L. (1970). *Origin of Eucaryotic Cells.* New Haven: Yale University Press.

———. (1981). *Symbiosis in Cell Evolution.* San Francisco: Freeman.

McFague, S. (1993). *The Body of God.* Minneapolis: Fortress.

McSherry, E., Ciulla, M., Salisbury, S., and Tsuang, D. (1987). *Social Compass* 35, 4: 515–37.

Maslow, A.H. (1964). *Religions, Values, and Peak Experiences.* Columbus: Ohio State University Press.

———. (1970). *Motivation and Personality.* 2d ed. New York: Harper and Row.

———. (1971). *The Farther Reaches of Human Nature.* New York: Viking.

Oman, D., and Reed, D. (1998). *American Journal of Public Health* 88: 1469–75.

Piaget, J. (1997). *The Moral Judgment of the Child.* New York: Free Press Paperbacks.

Polanyi, M. (1964). *Personal Knowledge: Towards a Postcritical Philosophy.* New York: Harper Torchbooks.

Shannon, C., and Weaver, W. (1949). *The Mathematical Theory of Communication.* Urbana: University of Illinois Press.

Specter, M. (2001). "Rethinking the Brain." Annals of Science. *The New Yorker,* July 23, 42–53.

Sperry; R.W. (1992). "Paradigms of Belief: Theory and Metatheory." *Zygon: Journal of Religion and Science* 26 (June): 237–58.

Suchocki, M.H. (1997). "Introduction." In *Trinity in Process: A Relational Theology of God,* ed. J.A. Bracken, S.J., and M.H. Suchocki. New York: Continuum.

Thilly, F., revised by Ledger Wood. (1952). *A History of Philosophy.* New York: Henry Holt.

Unamuno, M. de, n.d., Cited in *Discover,* Sep. 2001, p. 18.

Waldrop, M.M. (1992). *Complexity: The Emerging Science at the Edge of Order and Chaos.* New York: Simon & Schuster.

Wiener, P.P., ed. (1973). *Dictionary of the History of Ideas,* vol. 2. New York: Charles Scribner's Sons.

# Index

# Biographical Note

**Carol Rausch Albright** recently retired as co-director of the Midwest Region of the Science and Religion Course Program, operated by the Center for Theology and the Natural Sciences with support from the John Templeton Foundation. She shared this responsibility with her husband, John Albright, a physicist. Before assuming responsibility for the Midwest Region, the Albrights co-directed the program's Southeast Region. Carol Albright was for nine years executive editor of *Zygon: Journal of Religion and Science.* She serves as treasurer of the Center for Advanced Study in Religion and Science (CASIRAS), a corporation that co-sponsors both the journal *Zygon* and the Zygon Center for Religion and Science in Chicago, where Carol is an associate. Soon to be president of the American Theological Society, Midwest Region, Carol writes in the area of neuroscience and theology. Her publications include *The Humanizing Brain: Where Religion and Neuroscience Meet,* co-authored with James B. Ashbrook (Pilgrim, 1997); *Beginning with the End: God, Science and Wolfhart Pannenberg,* co-edited with Joel Haugen (Open Court, 1997); and *Where God Lives in the Human Brain,* co-authored with James B. Ashbrook (Sourcebooks, 2001).

# Other books in the Saint Paul University Research Series: Faith and Science

### Chaos Theology: A Revised Creation Theology
*By Sjoerd L. Bonting*

"I am privileged as an Anglican scientist-theologian to be allowed the opportunity to set forth a revised creation theology, which I call chaos theology, and to show its usefulness for the science–theology dialogue and a reconsideration of some important theological topics, even though this means abandoning the traditional *creatio ex nihilo* doctrine.

"My premise is that we have two world views, the theological and the scientific, both of which are God-given. These two world views, therefore, need not clash, but taken together should give us a deeper view of reality, provided we keep in mind the limitations of each. The scientific world view gives answers to the "How?" questions, while the theological world view responds to the "Why?" questions. The theologian may criticize the scientist when he falls into reductionism ("it is nothing but…"), while the scientist may take to task the theologian who makes statements that entail mechanisms that conflict with our scientific insight. Such is the case with *creatio ex nihilo,* as I try to demonstrate."

**Sjoerd L. Bonting** received a Ph.D. in biochemistry from the University of Amsterdam in 1952. He held various university and National Institute of Health positions in the United States until 1965, when he returned to the University of Amsterdam as Professor and Chairman of the Department of Biochemistry. From 1985 to 1993 he served as a scientific consultant to NASA's International Space Station project. Dr. Bonting was ordained a priest of the Episcopal Church in the United States in 1964, after completing theological studies.

# Towards a Theology of Science
### Donald J. Lococo, CSB

"We move 'towards' a theology of science because such a discipline does not yet exist. Science assumes that theology is a subjective world view that has nothing to do with 'real' knowledge; theology is baffled by the rapid advance of natural science on the basis of presuppositions that seem to overturn its most sacred beliefs. In circles where efforts are made to bridge the divide between science and religion, theology is often peripheral to the dialogue; the emphasis is placed on religion as an empirical phenomenon that can be justified according to the criterion of rationality of natural science.

"My remarks are mostly methodological. Drawing on the theology of Hans Urs von Balthasar and the hermeneutical philosophy of Hans-Georg Gadamer, I present the concept of *logos*, the notion of a rational ground of being, as a common presupposition of science and theology. I first sketch briefly a theological interpretation of the history of Western science as a history of *logos*: the origins of the concept in Greek philosophy; its enlargement in Christian theology; its reduction to the notion of numerical unity as natural science progressively emancipated itself from theology; and finally, the forgetting of the concept in the current postmodern fragmentation of knowledge. I then examine some of the methodological issues that divide theology and natural science, in particular the necessary methodological agnosticism of empirical science, the problem revelation poses for science as an argument from authority, the need for a renewed metaphysics to mediate the agnosticism of science with the faith of theology, and the possibilities opened up for a science–theology dialogue by Vatican II."

**Donald Joseph Lococo,** a priest of the Basilian order, is Assistant Professor of Christianity and Culture at the University of St. Michael's College in Toronto. Dr. Lococo received a Ph.D. in Zoology from the University of Toronto in 1985. He has since taught biology at the University of St. Thomas in Houston, Texas, and has published in both scientific and theological journals.

## Crucible of Creativity:
## Knowing God and Nature in a Postmodern World
*By Jitse M. van der Meer*

"Ever since St. Augustine, an important question in Western Christianity has been how faith and reason are related. Strangely, up to a decade ago, most of what was said and written about religion and science ignored the person, in whom knowing and believing are combined.

"I take a different approach by focussing on the person as creature. This is intended as a fundamental shift away from the rationalistic framework in terms of which religion and science were seen to be interacting for the past two thousand years. I argue that they are related in the person because it is the person who stands in relation to God and nature. I assess the role of some of the faculties of humankind that are involved in the engagement of religious beliefs and the explanation of natural phenomena. Among these faculties are cognition and religious believing. I consider them as natural characteristics with which we have been created. My key point will be that these faculties are related via a third faculty, that of the imagination. Together, these three faculties are 'a crucible of creativity.'"

**Jitse M. van der Meer** received a Ph.D in biology from the Catholic University of Nijmegen, the Netherlands, in 1978. After postdoctoral research and positions at Heidelberg and Purdue, Dr. van der Meer came to Redeemer College, where he is currently professor of biology. Dr. van der meer was the founding director of the Pascal Centre for Advanced Studies in Faith and Science and is its acting director.

To order, contact Novalis at 1-800-387-7164 or cservice@novalis.ca